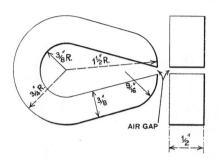

AIR GAP

Old-Time Secrets of

MAKING
PERMANENT
MAGNETS

*An anthology of simple techniques
used over the centuries to create
powerful permanent magnets.*

Lindsay Publications Inc

Old-Time Secrets of
Making Permanent Magnets

Reprinted by
Lindsay Publications Inc
Bradley IL 60915

ISBN 1-55918-305-5

2004

1   2   3   4   5   6   7   8   9   0

WARNING

Contents

The Operation and Manufacture of Magnetos – 1

by Harold Whiting Slauson

MACHINERY MAGAZINE ENGINEERING ED – OCTOBER 1910

Ever since the first internal combustion motor puffed and snorted and backfired, the ignition problem has been one of the most serious with which the designers have had to contend. In the early days the "hot tube" served as the source of heat by which the charge was "exploded," but this was adaptable only for low-speed, heavy-duty, inefficient, stationary engines, and was no more suited for automobile or motor boat practice than is flint and steel for a modern rapid-fire gun. The electric current has gradually been developed as the source of 'heat for ignition purposes, until now it may be said to be used on practically every internal combustion engine in existence. Its points of advantage over any of the other systems formerly in use lie in the fact that it furnishes a point or area of intense heat at the instant desired, and that the time during the stroke of the piston at which the ignition shall occur can be regulated by the operator. This makes it the only ignition source possible for use on high-speed motors.

Dry Batteries vs. Magneto Generator

It is only recently, however, that the electrical system of ignition has been brought to its present high efficiency, for the source of current has not always been as reliable as could be wished. Dry batteries depend upon a chemical action for the production of current, and they will deteriorate whether used or not. This renders continual testing necessary to make certain that the batteries are sufficiently strong for the day's run, and at best they are more or less capricious and liable to fail without previous warning. A storage battery will continue to give current until it has "run out," but it must be charged occasionally and its ingredients and plates must be attended to carefully, especially during freezing weather, so that it will not deteriorate rapidly or be utterly ruined. Consequently, although dry batteries or storage batteries form reliable sources of current while they last, the care, attention and renewals that they require if used frequently, make them more suitable as auxiliaries than as generators or storehouses of the main ignition supply.

Universal Application of Magneto Generator on Automobiles

During the last few years, the increase in the reliability of the automobile motor has been astonishing. From a machine which, a decade ago, could only be driven by an expert, to a car that can be handled by a woman or child, that will start on the first crank, and that will continue to run indefinitely, day and night, as long as it is fed with gasoline and oil, is a striking advance, but it would not be exaggerating to say that much of this change has been brought about by the almost universal application of the magneto on the modern automobile. The magneto generates current independent of storage capacity or chemical renewals, and consequently furnishes a source of ignition supply as long as power can be obtained with which to drive it. It is really a converter, or transformer of mechanical force into electrical energy, and as the small amount of power necessary to operate it is obtained from the motor to which it is furnishing current, it will generate the ignition supply without deterioration as long as required.

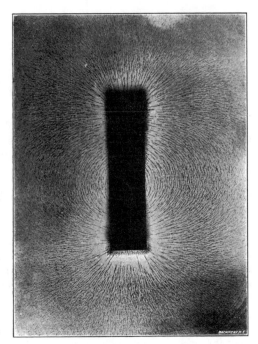

Fig. 1. Iron Filings showing the Lines of Force around a Bar Magnet

The Principle of the Magneto Generator

Although the appearance of the magneto is familiar to everyone who has ever driven a car or who has been interested in internal combustion motors in general, probably but a small percentage of these persons really understand the theory of the action and operation of the machine. It is in reality nothing but a small and compact form of dynamo with a few changes and refinements made necessary by the nature of its location and the' work that it is called upon to perform. Around every magnet. there are what are known as "lines of force" emanating from all portions, and concentrated chiefly at the extreme ends, or north and south poles of the magnet. The basic principle of the magneto, dynamo or generator, lies in the fact that if these lines of force are cut by a wire passing near the magnet at either the north or south poles, an electromotive force, or difference in pressure of an electric current, will be set up in this moving wire. In other words, a current of electricity is generated in this wire cutting the lines of

Fig. 2. Showing Lines of Force around the Poles of a U-shaped Magnet

poles of the magnet, or field. Through these notches in the armature and parallel to the axis, are wound several layers of insulated wire. This great number of wires cutting the lines of force of the field, serve to generate a greater current than would be the case were but one wire used, and consequently if the armature is driven at a high speed, and the magnetic fields are strong enough, electric power sufficient to light several lamps may be obtained from even the smallest machine. In the ordinary power-house generator, the fields are wound with insulated wire in order to form a separately-excited electromagnet. It is in this respect that the magneto differs chiefly from the dynamo, for the former has no electro-magnet, but uses instead, a permanent magnet. This consists of the U-shaped bar of iron, specially treated so that it will retain its magnetism for an indefinite period of time after it has once been magnetized.

Although the lines of force are, of course, invisible, their position and the effect made upon them by a rotating armature or series of wires cutting them transversely are well shown by the accompanying illustrations, Figs. 1 to 5, inclusive, which show iron filings in the field of a magneto. These illustrations were taken when the armature was

force, and if the ends of this wire are connected, a flow of the electric "fluid" will continue as long as the motion through the lines of force is kept up. If the magnet is bent U-shape, a moving wire, or series of wires, may cut the lines of force emanating from both poles without moving out of a position of rotation midway between the two poles. The magnet is known as the field of the machine, and the wire cutting the lines of force forms the armature – the two composing the principal parts of any electric generator or motor.

The armature generally consists of an iron spindle, notched out in several portions of its periphery, and rotating on a horizontal axis placed midway between the two placed in different positions, and show unusually well how the lines of force are collected or swept up,. by the revolving bundle of wires, and unite to form the electric current.

Lines of force from the north pole of a magnet cut by a wire or revolving °armature will induce a current in one direction through the circuit, while the current flows in the opposite direction if the lines of force from the south pole are cut. This means, then, that in the simplest form of magneto or dynamo in which the two ends of the armature wire are led to "collector rings," the current will flow first in one direction, and then in the other, as alternate poles of the field are cut by the revolving armature. This forms the alternating current, familiar to most people.

Practically all magnetos that are geared to the motor are of the type producing alternating current.

Principle of the
Direct-current Magneto

In equipping old automobile motors and marine and stationary engines with magnetos, however, it is sometimes impracticable to install a set of gears, and in this event the use of a direct-current magneto is advisable. The direct-current machine is the opposite of the alternating type in that any point in the circuit always has a north and south pole. In other words, the direction of the flow of current is constant, and not changeable, as it is in the alternating type. In order to keep the current flowing in the same direction, a slightly different type of armature must be used in the direct-current type than is found in the alternating machine. Such an armature generally has several slots cut in its periphery, parallel to the axis of rotation, and in each pair of these slots, on opposite sides of the armature, are wound a few turns of insulated wire. A copper commutator or drum, is placed on the armature shaft near the terminals of these turns of wire. This commutator has as many

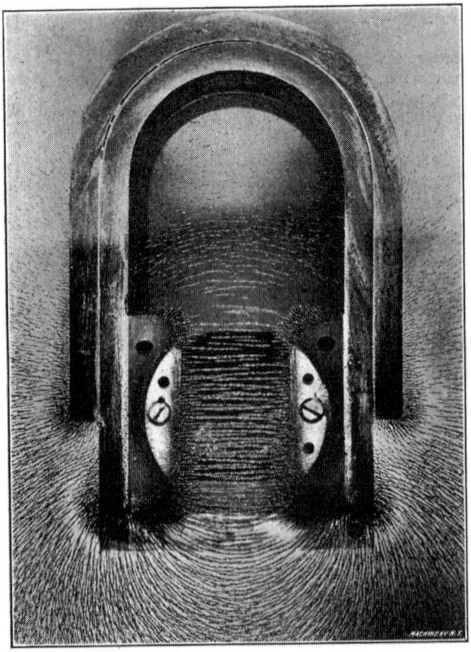

Fig. 3. Compound U-shaped Magnet with Pole Pieces and Armature showing Action of Lines of Force

segments on its surface as there are slots in the periphery of the armature, and each bundle of wires is soldered to its own segment, which is thoroughly insulated from all the rest. Two copper or carbon brushes are placed 180 degrees apart in contact with the armature, and continually wipe against it as the armature revolves. As each bundle of wires passes by one pole of the field it induces a current which flows in one direction, and this is collected by the brush on that side and sent out into the circuit. By the time this same section of the armature reaches the other pole of the field and is excited with a current in the reverse direction, its segment. of the commutator wipes against the opposite brush and the electricity thus collected flows through the circuit. In other words, one brush collects all the current when the windings of the armature are positively excited by reason of proximity to one pole, and the opposite brush collects all the negative current from the armature when it is cutting the lines of force of the other end of the magnet.

The Function of the Distributor

Although the field and armature are the primary parts of an electric generator, there are several other attachments to a magneto which are vitally necessary for the successful application of the machine to an automobile ignition system. One of these is the distributor, which is the hard rubber box, generally located on top of the magneto, from which the wires that lead to the separate cylinders of the car emerge. By means of a hard rubber disk, in the periphery of which is a copper segment connected with the source of current supply, connection is made with the spark plugs of the various cylinders in the proper order. This distributor enables a single unit coil to take the place of the four coils usually found on the dash of all cars using a battery ignition system. In some systems, to be considered later, no

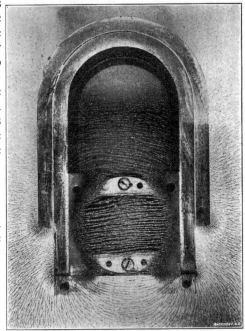

Fig. 4. Same as Fig. 3. Armature rotated One-fourth Turn. Note Change in Lines of Force

9

coil whatsoever is used, the current being led directly from the magneto to the spark plugs of the cylinders.

Various Systems of Ignition in Gas Engines

There are two systems of gas engine ignition, for either of which a magneto may be used advantageously. These are known as the make-and-break and the jump-spark systems. The spark, or flash, rather, in the former is obtained by sending a comparatively low-voltage current through a mechanism passing through the cylinder walls. At the proper time, two portions of this mechanism break

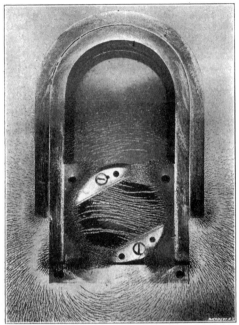

Fig. 5. Showing Lines of Force with Armature in Position Midway between those of Figs. 3. and 4.

or snap off, and the result of this break in the circuit is a hot flash, which serves to ignite the charge in the cylinder. The same result will be obtained in the open air if the two terminals of a set of batteries are taken in the hand, connected, and then separated with a "wiping" motion. A bright flash will be seen, which corresponds to the igniting spark of the make-and-break system.

The Jump-spark System of Ignition

The jump-spark system is in more common use than the make-and-break, and is especially well-adapted for magneto service. This system is so well known that it is useless to describe it in detail,

10

and suffice it to say that when the connection is made, the current jumps across a small gap between two points of the spark plug screwed into the cylinder, and in so jumping, a hot spark is formed. Although this space is scarcely ever more than 1/32 inch wide, it is well known that a high voltage is required to cause a current to jump even an infinitesimal gap, and as the hot gases and compression in the cylinder increase the resistance, it is necessary to furnish a sufficiently high electromotive force to the current to enable the spark to jump at least half an inch in the open air. This requires a pressure of from 10,000 to 20,000 volts, and because of the high voltage used, this is known as the "high-tension" system. The make-and-break type of ignition, by virtue of its lower voltage, is known as the *"low-tension"* system.

Principles of the High-tension Magneto

Batteries, of course, cannot furnish this tremendous voltage required for the jump spark, and it is the duty of the coils to "step up" the current to the final fifteen or twenty thousand volts. A "step up" transformer consists of two coils, one within the other, known as the primary and secondary. The current from the source of supply is led through the coarser, or primary winding, and this "induces" a very high voltage current in the many turns of fine wire of the secondary winding. The amperage is reduced, however, in the proportion in which the voltage is raised. In order to induce this high voltage in the secondary winding, there must be an intermittent surging, or "piling up," of the original current. This is accomplished by means of a vibrator, or interrupter, through which the primary current passes, and by the alternate making and breaking of the contact through the medium of a magnet and spring the desired intermittent action is obtained.

A direct-current magneto can be introduced into the above mentioned system of ignition, the vibrating coils being used in connection with this mechanical source of current in the same manner as with the batteries. In this case the magneto may be driven by either a belt or a friction pulley,

and the necessity for any gears in this connection is eliminated.

The ordinary alternating-current magneto furnishing current for a high-tension ignition system, however, operates on a slightly different principle. In .this case a non vibrating coil is used, of the same general design as the step-up transformer previously described, but without the current-interrupting mechanism. Consequently the magneto itself is equipped with an interrupter in the form of a cam revolving in intermittent contact with one or more rocker arms, on the end of each of which is a platinum contact point through which the current passes when the cam forces that end of the rocker arm against another platinum point, and thus completes the circuit. This cam is generally attached to the end of the armature shaft, and is so timed that the circuit is closed whenever the armature is in such a position that it will deliver a maximum amount of current. This interrupter, or circuit-breaker, is used as the timer, the spark being advanced or retarded in the cylinders as the case containing the contact points is revolved forward or backward on the armature shaft. Because the current from the magneto is not absolutely constant, it is necessary that the machine be geared positively to the crankshaft of the motor in the proper relation so that connection will be made with the spark plugs through the timer only when the armature is receiving its maximum amount of current. In the ordinary four-cylinder motor magneto there are generally two high-voltage im-

11

pulses, or contacts of the cam, for each revolution of the armature.

Some magnetos are made which will furnish a high-tension current without the necessity of a step-up coil, or transformer. Such a machine has two windings on the armature, the primary and secondary, so that in reality the transformer is combined with the armature, instead of being located in a separate box on the dash. A machine of this type is a bona-fide high-tension magneto, because the current is generated at the same high voltage as that at which it will be used in the plugs. The other type of magnetos, however, is sometimes erroneously called "high-tension" when used for jump-spark work, even though the current is actually generated at a low voltage in the machine, but it will be seen that these are actually of the low-tension type with a separate step-up coil to obtain the desired electromotive force. There should be some method of distinguishing between the two types, but because both systems are used for jump-spark service, the majority of persons seem to think that th same name will serve for each of these two entirely different forms

The Operation and Manufacture of Magnetos – 2

by Harold Whiting Slauson
MACHINERY MAGAZINE ENGINEERING ED – NOVEMBER 1910

Not only are the majority of motor cars now built equipped with magnetos, but the older types of automobiles and new and second-hand marine and stationary engines are being supplied with this form of ignition as well, and this has created such a demand that it may be said that the annual production of magnetos in this country, alone, can be counted by the hundreds of thousands. The magneto is a delicate machine to construct and assemble and the greatest precision and accuracy are required in finishing its various parts, some of which are shown in Fig. 6. The magneto and its parts are designated as follows:

A High-tension magneto, assembled.

B Magnets composing field of magneto.

C Frame in which armature is mounted.

D Pole piece – forming extension of magnetic field in order partially to surround the revolving armature. There are two such pole pieces.

E Armature and driving gear.

F Timer, or circuit breaker, mechanism and case.

G Distributer case back.

H Timer cover.

I Screw and spring holding timer cover in place.

J Distributer case front and high-tension wire terminals.

K   Driving end bearing and case.
L   Distributer gear and sector.

Making the Permanent Magnets

One of the most interesting, as well as the most important,

of force could be re-established. Consequently it is necessary so to treat the steel that the magnetism will be retained permanently. Soft iron is unsuitable for this purpose, as it will not retain its magnetism unless in contact with another magnet, or except while excited by a current of electricity passing through a surrounding winding of wire. In many instances the permanent magnets are made of tungsten steel. This is cut into bars

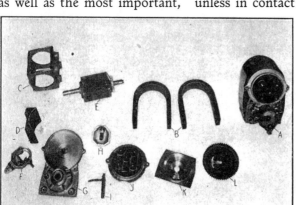

Fig. 6. Component Parts of High-tension Magneto

features of the construction of a magneto is the manufacture of the permanent magnets that are used to form the magnetic fields of the machine. Should these lose their magnetism, the machine would be rendered useless until the lines

of the proper length, and each is heated to a cherry-red. Fig. 7 shows the method of shaping a magnet as used in the manufacture of the Kurtz magneto, a Indianapolis, Ind. When heated to the proper temperature, the

Fig. 7. Bending Magnets to Shape from Bar Steel in the Hercules Electric Works

bar is placed in the clamp, which has already been set at exactly the proper width to hold it firmly in place. A center block, constituting the form around which the magnet is bent serves as the other jaw of the clamp, and is curved at one end to the proper shape for the inside of the magnet. On a long handle, which is pivoted to the under side of this block, is fastened a hardened-steel roller which swings with the handle and follows, in a concentric curve, the shape of the. former. This combination of roller and lever serves to bend the magnet to the proper U-shape very quickly, only a few seconds being required from the time the bar leaves the fire until it is ready for the final heat-treating process.

Hardening the Magnets

After being heated for the proper length of time in a fire of absolutely constant temperature, as shown in Fig. 8, the magnets are cooled in water. As the magnets have already been formed to the proper shape and size, it is undesirable that they should contract to any appreciable extent in the cooling process, and in consequence, each is suspended

in the tank of water in a special clamp, which is shown at if resting against the pile of magnets. This device holds the magnet rigidly in the proper shape, and as the jaws of the clamp consist of a few small points, the water can reach practically all parts of the surface of the steel.

Charging the Magnets

After these shaping and heat-treating processes are completed, the magnet is ready to receive – and to hold permanently, presumably – the magnetism with which it may be "charged." This magnetizing is accomplished by placing the embryo magnet in two upright, parallel, hollow bars, around each of which are wound many turns of wire, and through which an electric current is passed. This forms an electromagnet of the two hollow bars, one being the north pole, and the other the south pole, and this induces magnetism of the opposite kind in the ends of the magnets placed therein. In other words, the end of the permanent magnet placed

Fig. 8. Heat Treating the Magnets after they have been bent to Shape in the Hercules Electric Works

14

in the hollow bar constituting the north pole of the electro-magnet, is charged with the opposite kind of lines of force, and this becomes the south pole of the completed permanently-magnetized piece. In like manner, the opposite process takes place in the other pole and the hollow bar. While this magnetizing process is going on, the magnet must be tapped several times in order to distribute and help arrange the molecules properly – for it is on the re-adjustment of the molecules composing the bar of special steel that the magnetism of the completed piece depends. Where magnets are manufactured in large quantities, a special machine, or battery of machines, is provided to facilitate the process. This consists of the wire-wound hollow bars, as described above, and a belt-driven spider on which are four or five radial arms, each terminating in a light hammer-head. This spider is revolved rapidly, and is mounted in such a position that the hammer-heads strike the piece to be magnetized with the proper amount of force. Each magnet is kept in this machine for from ten to thirty seconds, and is then tested for its magnetism. Each magnet is tested thereafter several times during the succeeding twenty-four hours to make certain that there is no loss of magnetism during that period, and if at the end of the day it still shows its maximum strength, it is assumed that it will retain this residual magnetism permanently.

Casting the Bronze Parts

Bronze castings are required in the manufacture of a magneto, and the foundry is by no means the least important part of a well-equipped plant. In one of the largest magneto factories, 8000 castings are made daily, and in order to accomplish this enormous production, duplicate patterns are used extensively. In some instances, as many as 32 duplicate parts will be cast in the same flask at once, and in order to minimize the danger of imperfect molds, pneumatic machines are used for separating the flasks, and compressed air vibrators for loosening the sand around the pattern. Each casting is inspected thoroughly so that only perfect pieces can reach the rough-stock room.

Making the Armatures

After the castings have been machined, those that are to be used as the cores of armatures, coils, or fields are taken to the winding room Where they receive the required number of layers of wire. It is important that there should be the proper number of turns of wire in each part of magneto or coil, as it is upon this that the output of the machine, or the proportional increase in voltage delivered by the transformer depends. Most of the winding is done by girls, who become very dexterous at the work. The simple "spool windings" for coils and the like can be made on a high-speed winding machine, but the more complicated process of the manufacture of a direct-current armature requires hand work almost entirely. Fig. 9 shows the winding department of the Remy Electric Co., Anderson,

Fig. 9 The Winding Room of the Remy Electric Co., in which 2500 Miles of Wire are used per Day

16

Ind., where over 2500 miles of insulated wire is used daily in the manufacture of the armature and coils. In order to make certain that the proper amount of wire has been put on each winding, and to discover if there are any short circuits or breaks in the insulation, each piece is tested for its resistance by sending a given current of electricity through the winding and observing the readings of the ammeter and voltmeter introduced into the circuit.

Impregnating the Armature Windings

After having been wound, tested, and found perfect, the coils, armatures, or fields, as the case may be, are taken to the impregnating room, shown in Fig. 10, where they receive their covering of insulating varnish or wax in order the

the vacuum is then changed to a high pressure, thus compressing the liquid wax or varnish into all the interstices of the winding and rendering leakage of current almost an impossibility.

Making the Small Parts of a Magneto

The small parts of a magneto, such as screws, cam, armature shaft, bearings, and the like, require such absolute precision in their manufacture that hand and automatic screw machines, and other automatic machines will be found to play an important part in the well-equipped magneto plant. Fig. 11 shows the screw machine

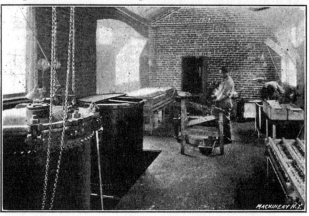

Fig. 10. Impregnating Room in which Coils are treated with Melted Wax or Insulating Varnish

more thoroughly to separate the individual wires from each other and to protect the whole winding from the outside air and dampness. The impregnating materials are reduced by steam to a liquid state, and the coils to be insulated are heated in a vacuum. Without reducing the vacuum, the impregnating material is turned in, and

department of the Remy Electric Co. Limit plug gages are used in testing all collars to within 0.001 inch, and in some instances, 0.0005 inch is the limit of variation allowed. In the above named plant each individual part is inspected and tested for size after each operation; and in this manner, a completed part, which may have

17

Fig. 11. Battery of Automatic Screw Machines – Each Piece is inspected at the Machine before the Next Operation

passed through the hands of ten or a dozen workmen, will not have to be discarded because of imperfections developed in its earlier stages of manufacture. There is an inspector ready to examine every consignment of parts as it is finished by each screw machine, and on completion, instead of being sent to the finished stock room, as is generally the case, all pieces are collected at one end of the machine shop for small parts. Here they are assembled, without having been moved more than twenty feet from the machines in which they were made. In other words, the machining, inspecting, and assembling are all performed in the one large room, and there is a minimum amount of transportation of the parts.

Making the Brass Terminals for the Remy Magneto

In the Remy magneto, the high tension wires to the cylinders lead from hard rubber sockets terminating in a split brass shank which has a hole drilled in it of the proper size to give a spring

fit to the terminal of the distributer with which each is connected. Each brass terminal is turned out in an automatic machine, and the hole is then drilled in the rounded end. The slotting is done by a special machine built at the factory. This machine consists of a belt-driven circular saw revolving at high speed in a vertical plane. Below this in the same plane, and driven slowly in the same direction by a small belt is a drum in two sections. This drum has threaded holes at frequent intervals in its periphery along the line where the two sections join. One of these sections is divided into segments, each of which is operated by a stationary cam as the drum revolves, thus causing each hole to open and close automatically. The operator places a piece in each hole as it revolves before him, and as this point of the periphery of the drum approaches the saw, the cam closes the jaw and holds the work solidly in position while the brass terminal is revolved through the lower edge of the saw. On the other side of the saw, the jaw is opened

18

by the cam, and the work drops into a trough. An experienced and quick operator can slot with this machine forty or fifty brass terminals a minute.

Construction of
the Direct-current Armature

As has been stated before, the armature of the direct-current magneto is much more complicated than that of the alternating-current type. The latter is a simple forging, shaped to receive one continuous winding. The direct-current armature, however, not only has at least six parts of separate windings, or a dozen slots, but in many instances it is built up of thin disks to form a laminated core. The armature of the Kurtz direct-current magneto is manufactured in this manner, and from long experience, it has been found that the best results are obtained if each disk is forced on the armature shaft separately instead of the entire hundred or so forming the armature core being lined up and pressed on all together. Each disk is punched from sheet steel, and is forced on the armature shaft with its companions as shown in Fig. 12. The armature shaft is held in place in a drill chuck having an attachment with a flat face which permits the first disk to be forced on to exactly the proper place. Each disk is held' in the proper position so that the slots will line up, by means of a fixture in the bed of the machine. This fixture has a hole in its center to receive the armature shaft, and two pins on its outer edge engage corresponding slots on the disk and serve to hold it steady. The feed handle is released and the armature shaft and chuck are dropped with considerable force on the fixture and disk, thus forcing the latter into position. The shaft is raised by means of the feed handle and the rack and pinion, and another disk is placed in position on the fixture. Although this may seem like a tedious operation, one man and one machine build up a complete armature of this type in a couple of minutes, and consequently can keep the winding room supplied easily.

Fig. 12. "Building up" the Laminated Armature of the Direct-current Magneto in the Kurtz Magneto Factory.

Making the Terminal Sockets

Hard rubber is the material best suited for confining the high-tension current within its proper limits, and consequently the terminal sockets, the distributer cover and box, and the distributor disk are all made of this substance. The rubber is molded to shape from soft sheets into which the vulcanizing chemicals have already been introduced. Aluminum molds are used into which the soft rubber, after having been heated on a steam table, is crowded and packed tightly by expert workmen. As there are only a comparatively few different shapes of hard rubber used on a single magneto, the molding and vulcanizing process becomes a duplicate-part-production of the highest type. This will be better realized when it is stated that three and four thousand Separate molds are placed in the vulcanizing ovens in a single "heat." Each mold will contain a certain number of ounces or fractions of an ounce of the soft rubber, and it is cut exactly to this weight before the molding process begins. There is consequently no waste whatsoever, and but a minimum amount of time is consumed in packing the molds. The soft rubber is heated in the molds in the vulcanizing oven for several hours. After withdrawal from the oven, the rubber is still soft, but it becomes hard upon being cooled slowly, and after the proper holes have been drilled, is ready for installation on the magneto.

Testing the Magneto

There is such a variety of conditions in the manufacture of the various parts that will affect the performance of the completed magneto, that the testing of the finished machine is an absolute necessity, even though the individual pieces have previously received several inspections. The great difficulty first encountered in the use of a magneto for ignition purposes was due to the fact that it seemed almost impossible to construct a machine that would give a sufficiently hot spark at low speeds of the motor, and yet one which could also be turned at several thousand revolutions with no danger of burning out the coil or other parts of the electric circuit. This difficulty has been successfully overcome, however, by the use of the proper strength of magnets and kind and amount of wire, and the modern magneto will deliver a hot spark at 140 revolutions of the armature shaft, and yet do equally satisfactory work when revolved at twenty times that speed. It is to satisfy the inspector that such is the case, that the magnetos receive their final test. For this purpose, several machines under the charge of one tester will be belted to a common pulley shaft and revolved at various speeds. As shown in Fig. 13 half a dozen Kurtz magnetos are belted in this manner, four spark plugs are connected by high-tension wires to the distributer terminals of each machine. The nature of the spark delivered by the machine to each plug may be observed in this manner for any speed of the

Fig. 13. Testing the Kurtz Alternating current Magnetos by Belt Power

armature. The clamps shown in the illustration passing over each magneto are attached to the testing bench, and are skeet-iron strips used for holding the machines in place while they are belted to the pulley shaft.

Inasmuch as a direct-current magneto does not need to be geared positively to the crankshaft of the motor, a friction or belt drive is generally used. It is advisable that the armature of the direct-current machine should revolve at approximately the same speed at all times, and consequently a governor attachment is usually provided with the driving device. In testing out a machine of this type, the bed is clamped firmly in position and the friction pulley placed in contact with the periphery of a rapidly-revolving wheel, as shown in Fig. 14. This would give a high speed to the armature of the magneto were it not for the governor, and the readings of the voltmeter placed above the wheel indicate whether the regulating device is properly adjusted or not. The

Fig. 14. Testing the Spark Delivered by the Friction-driven Direct-current Magneto. The Spark can be seen jumpng between the Ends of the Two Wires between the Terminals of the Coils in the Foreground

nature and strength of the spark can be determined in this case by the use of an ordinary vibrating coil and two wires between the high-tension terminals forming a variable gap. The spark is shown in the illustration in question. The other machine shown in this view is a "dummy field" and frame in which all armatures are mounted before final assembly in their respective magnetos. It is known that the magnets composing this dummy field are of the proper strength, and any poor results obtained in the test indicate that the armature is at fault, the discovery thus being made before the final assembly and testing of the machine for which the faulty armature was intended.

The Final Testing

An interesting final test is given to all machines in the Remy factory. Here, also, each magneto is tested for the spark it will deliver at both low and high speeds, but instead of using spark plugs, four variable gaps are provided for each machine. These variable gaps are mounted on a switchboard, each having one fixed terminal and one in the form of a swinging lever which can be moved by hand. The spark is observed with each gap set at the same distance as will be found in an ordinary spark plug, and then this distance is gradually increased until the spark ceases to jump. Three of the gaps are then closed entirely so that the current can easily pass from one terminal to the other with no obstruction, and the fourth switch is opened to a width of two or three inches. Although the whole generating power of the magneto is concentrated at this one gap, the current from so small a machine cannot, of course, jump such a distance. This causes the magneto to "work against itself," and if there were any imperfections or weaknesses in the windings of the machine or coil, they would be certain to assert themselves under such strenuous conditions.

When a modern magneto has once been tested and leaves

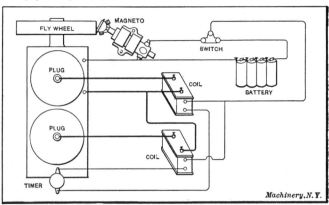

Fig. 15. Diagram of Wiring for a Two-cylinder Jump Spark. This also shows how a Friction-driven Direct-current Magneto may be introduced in the Ignition System to replace a Second Set of Batteries

the factory in perfect condition, it is seldom that it will fail to perform its duty if directions are carefully followed. It cannot be denied, however, that the magneto, though reliable, is a delicate machine, and for this reason no one but an expert, or, preferably, the manufacturer himself, should ever try to readjust or repair a faulty instrument. Even those who understand perfectly the theory of the magneto may be puzzled by some minor adjustment, and it is far better to follow directions and "Return magneto to factory in case of trouble."

The Process of Manufacturing Permanent Magnets

By F.B. Hays

MACHINERY MAGAZINE ENGINEERING ED – SEPT 1911

Permanent magnets are used on magnetos, tools, slot machines, toys, voltmeters, ammeters, speedometers, telephones, wattmeters, ignition devices, recording instruments, compasses, controlling devices, physical instruments, and switches. The magnets used on these devices are of various shapes and sizes. the illustration, Fig. 1, representing the most common forms in use at the present time.

The extensive use of permanent magnets, together with scientific methods of manufacturing them, has come about only in recent years. Ten years ago the production of permanent magnets was a branch of manufacturing of very little consequence, while today it is one of the important phases of the steel-working industry. Every plant making permanent magnets has its own process of manufacture, but the underlying

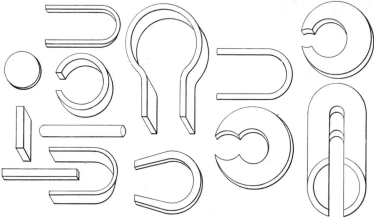

Fig. 1. A Collection of Various Types and Shapes of Permanent Magnets

and fundamental principles for the production of successful magnets are the same in all. A summary of these methods is given in this article.

Steel Used
for Making the Magnets

Permanent magnets are made from alloy steels. The composition of these steels is governed to a large extent by the various purposes for which the magnets are to be used. For instance, telephone magnets are made from 50- to 60-point carbon steel containing a high manganese content. Where a stronger magnet is required, as for magnetos, a 50- to 60-point carbon steel with a 3 to 7 per cent tungsten content is used.

Magnet steel is hard and tough before hardening, and its physical properties closely resemble those of low carbon tool steel. In several plants the scrap from the magnet department is used for lathe and planer tool sin the machine shop. After hardening (chilling), the steel becomes as hard and nearly as brittle as glass. Magnet steel is rolled into bars and sheets of any desired size. Bar magnets such as are used on wattmeters and most magnetos are made from bars, while plate magnets such as those in telephone receivers and on some types of magnetos are made from sheets. The principal requisites of a good magnet steel are uniformity of composition, freedom from blow-holes and seams, high magnetic qualities, retentivity, and freedom from cracks and blisters after treating.

Synopsis of the Methods
of Making Magnets

The process of making permanent bar magnets may be divided into five distinctive steps, as follows: (1) Testing the steel; (2) cutting the bars to proper lengths; (3) heating and forging; (4) heating and hardening; (5) grinding and magnetizing. For plate magnets, the process is shorter: (1) Testing the steel; (2) punching the plates from the sheet metal; (3) grinding and magnetizing.

Testing the Steel

Magnet steel is usually tested both at the steel mill and at the plant where it is used, to determine the proper "heats", and the magnetic qualities of the steel. Several methods are employed to determine this information, the most efficient of which is the following: Test bars and plates of magnet steel, as well as magnet forgings, which have been treated at different heats are tested for strength, permeability, and retentivity by means of a direct-reading permeameter. The results of these tests show the best temperatures for treating the steel, and also furnish complete data regarding its magnetic qualities. This method is used in the large steel mills and also in most modern magnet manufacturing shops. A direct-reading permeameter which is used for testing the magnet steel bars is shown in Fig. 2. This instrument is made by the Esterline Co., Lafayette, Ind.

Fig. 2. Esterline Permeameter used for Testing Magnet Steel

Cutting Magnet Bars to Required Lengths

The bars of magnet steel are obtained of the proper width and thickness, and then are sheared to the short lengths required for the magnets. The shears used for this purpose must be of massive construction, low geared, and provided with a heavy fly, wheel to overcome the sudden resistance offered by the hard-steel bars. The shaft driving the moving head must be adequately large or it will be twisted off when the shear blade strikes a hard spot in the steel, which frequently happens.

Some form of stop must be provided to accurately gage the length to which the bars are cut off. This stop must be strong and rigid and provided with some means of adjustment in order that it may be varied to suit the required length of the bars to be cut. The stop is usually placed on the opposite side from that at which the bar is fed, so that the operator may quickly push the bar through the jaws of the shear until its movement

Fig. 3. Shearing Magnet Bars to the Required Lengths

25

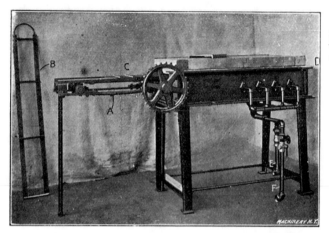

is arrested by one end of the bar butting against the stop.

The illustration, Fig. 3, shows a shear used for cutting the bars to the length required for the magnet. A is the bar of magnet steel, B the shearing blades, C a guide bar, to prevent the bar from tilting when it is being sheared, and D a stop for regulating the length of the piece being sheared. The stop D is adjusted along the threaded studs E, and when in the desired position is locked by the lock-nuts F.

Forging

Practically all forms of bar magnets require one or more forging operations, to give them the proper shape. Forging operations on magnets are often termed "heating and bending", or "heating and forming", as the short

bars (cut to the proper length by the shear) are heated and then bent to the required shapes. The bars are heated to from 1472 to 1652 degrees F. (according to predetermined temperature tests) in coke, oil, or gas furnaces made especially for this work. The illustra-

Fig. 5. Coke Furnace for Heating Bar Magnets for Bending – Bar Magnets shown at A

tions Figs. 4, 5 and 6 and Fig. 8 at A show the four types of furnaces used. The heating temperature is regulated by electric pyrometers, as shown in Fig. 10. Coke furnaces are rapidly being superseded by oil and gas furnaces, as the latter can be more accurately regulated and produce better results.

The most recent development in this line is a furnace made by the American Gas Furnace Co., shown in Fig. 4. This furnace is equipped with a power-driven endless chain A. upon which is placed the carrier B loaded with the short magnet bars. The carrier moves slowly from left to right, the cold bars entering at C, being heated to the required temperature and discharged at D, at the rate of about six bars a minute. E is the gas inlet and F the air blast inlet.

After heating, the bars are placed one at a time in some form of power press, usually a very powerful and massive bull, dozer or vertical press, as shown at B, Fig. 8. These machines are equipped with special dies (those for forming a U-shaped magnet in a bulldozer being shown in Fig. 11), which bend the bar to the correct shape. Simple magnets such as those of the horseshoe type require only one bending operation, whereas more complicated shapes require two or three bending operations. Extremely irregular shapes which are not used in great quantity are bent bY hand as shown in Fig. 7. This machine consists of a cast-

Fig. 7. Forming Odd-shaped Magnets by Hand

27

Fig. 8.
Heating and
Bending
Magnet
Forgings in
the Sangamo
Electric Co.'s
Plant

Fig. 9.
Grinding
Magnet
Forgings

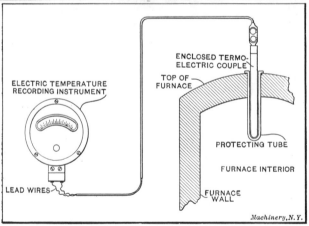

Fig. 10. Showing Application of an Electric Pyrometer to Magnet
Heating Furnace

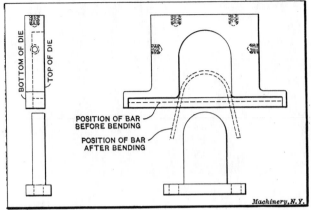

Fig. 11. Punch and Die used for Forming U-shaped Magnets in a Bulldozer

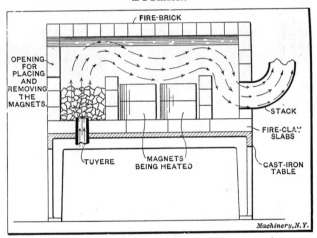

Fig. 12. Section of Coke Furnace for Heating Magnets previous to Hardening

iron die around which a steel roller is revolved by means of a lever to which the roller is pinned. One end of the hot bar is fastened to the die by a clamping device, so that the bar is held between the roller and the die. The lever is pulled around the die by the operator, causing the roller to press the heated bar against the die, and thus bending the bar to the desired shape.

Hardening

The forged magnet bars are now allowed to cool. slowly in order to prevent crystallization. They are then ground on disk grinders or emery wheels to the proper lengths, as shown in Fig. 9, and drilled or machined if so required by the specifications. After this they are placed in the hardening furnace, and brought

Fig. 13. Hardening Magnet Forgins in the Sangamo Electric Co.'s Plant

Fig. 14. A Gas Furnace for Hardening Magnets, equipped with a Conveyor

to a temperature of from 1500 to 1600 degrees F. (as determined by previous tests).. The temperature must be very accurately regulated as a variation of only a few degrees is likely to injure the steel.

Coke, oil and gas furnaces are used as shown in Figs. 12, 13, and 14. Oil and gas furnaces give the best results, but are more costly and more expensive to operate than coke furnaces. The difficulties experienced with coke furnaces are due to the impurities-in the coke, such as sulphur and

30

silicon, being absorbed by the steel at the high temperature maintained. However, the fault is almost entirely overcome in a furnace constructed as shown in Fig. 12.

Fig. 14 shows a gas furnace similar to the one described for heating magnet bars for bending (Fig. 4). The magnet forgings A enter the furnace at B and are discharged at C at the rate of about four a minute. The magnet forgings shown in this illustration are for use in electric meters..

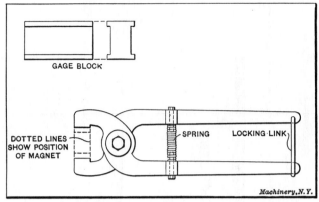

Fig. 15. Tongs and Gage Block for Holding Magnets while Hardening to prevent them from Springing out of Shape

When the magnet forgings reach the required temperature they are removed from the hardening furnace and plunged into cold running water or brine, where they are allowed to remain until cold; their are then removed and piled up ready for grinding and magnetizing. When magnets of very accurate dimensions are required, such as those used on magnetos, the forgings are placed in special tongs with gage-blocks between them, as shown in Fig. 15, to prevent them from warping while cooling. A typical group of tongs for handling heated magnets is shown in Fig. 17. Magnet forgings of complicated shape are frequently annealed before hardening, in order to insure uniform heating.

Grinding and Magnetizing

After being removed from the cooling bath, the forgings are ground to the specified dimensions and all scale and rough edges removed. They are then ready for magnetizing.

Magnetizing is accomplished by means of electro-magnets, solenoids, or a combination of the two. One of the most efficient devices for this purpose is shown in Fig. 16, in which A is the magnet being magnetized, B the shell of the solenoid, (7 the winding of the solenoid, D the insulating covering, and E the malleable iron electro-magnetic field piece. While the magnet is being magnetized, the current is rapidly interrupted and the magnet hammered with a rawhide mallet to cause the magnetic molecules to properly adjust themselves. From ten to twenty seconds is usually required for each magnet. This is the last operation required in making permanent magnets. After magnetizing they are ready for use and will retain their magnetism for years under ordinary conditions.

Plate Magnets

Plate magnets are stamped out of sheet magnet steel 1/16 inch to 5/32 inch thick, by means of ordinary punch presses equipped with

31

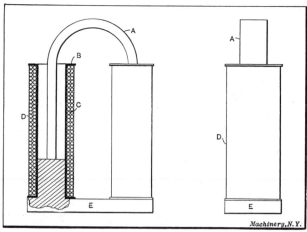

Fig. 16. Magnetizing a U-shaped Magnet

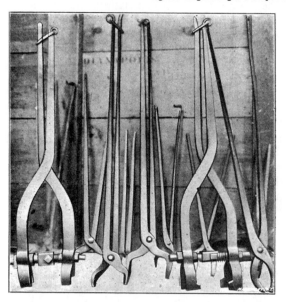

Fig. 17. A Group of Tongs for Handling Heated Magnets

hardened steel punches and dies. The process is practically the same as that used for making any form of flat stamping. The stampings require no grinding, drilling or machining before hardening. The method of hardening is similar to that used for other forms of magnets, except that special care must be observed to prevent warping, and to keep the hardening heat from being blanketed by accumulation of scale on the surface. The means used for grinding and magnetizing are similar to those

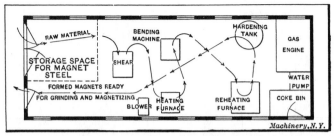

Fig. 18. Plan of Magnet Forming Department of Hercules Electric Co.
Arrows indicate Movement of Stock

used for bar magnets.

Conclusion

The manufacture of permanent magnets, although a comparatively new industry, has reached a place of considerable importance both from a monetary and scientific standpoint. Its rapid growth may be attributed to the extensive use of this type of magnet in electrical measuring instruments, magnetos, telephones, and recording instruments. The scientific production methods employed are due largely to the constant demand of magneto manufacturers for powerful magnets that will retain their magnetism for an indefinite period under all sorts of adverse conditions, and which will at the same time be absolutely accurate in size and shape. Taken as a whole few branches of industry represent a more interesting study from a chemical, mechanical, and electrical standpoint than the manufacture of permanent magnets.

Steel for Permanent Magnets

MACHINERY MAGAZINE ENGINEERING ED – SEPT 1913

Steel containing 5-1/2 per cent tungsten makes excellent permanent magnets. The steel should be heated above the recalescence point and when quenched should show a fine-grained fracture. After magnetizing a magnet should be "aged" by prolonged heating in boiling water or steam. A short bar magnet tends to lose its magnetism quickly; the coefficient of demagnetization for a bar magnet twenty-five diameters in length is 0.05 while that of a magnet five diameters long is 0.5, or ten times as great. A bar magnet five hundred diameters long is supposed to be permanent. The magnetic force of the best magnets is considered by Prof. S. P. Thompson to be only 60 to 80 per cent of what may be eventually attained.

Recharging Permanent Magnets

MACHINERY MAGAZINE ENGINEERING ED – DECEMBER 1913

A.B. – I would like some information on recharging the permanent magnets of ignition magnetos for automobiles and motorcycles. Customers come to my shop to have their magnetos recharged, but I have not been able to handle the work successfully. I have wound coils for recharging and have followed the prescribed directions for magnetizing but with indifferent success. The magnetic flux would be very strong, but as soon as the current was shut off the magnet would be little or no stronger than before. I have annealed the magnets, thinking that by annealing and rehardening the original magnetic strength could be imparted again. Any information that the readers of Machinery can give we on this subject will be much appreciated.

Recharging Permanent Magnets

MACHINERY MAGAZINE ENGINEERING ED – JANUARY 1914

In the How and Why department of Machinery for December I note that A.B. has trouble in retaining magnetism in permanent magnets of magnetos. In the first place, the steel should be very hard, as this is an important feature of permanent magnets. As the magnetic flux is strong when the current is on, the current evidently flows in the proper direction; the trouble is elsewhere. I have magnetized permanent magnets with success by tapping them with a hammer while in the magnetic field. The sharp hammer blows seem to help the magnets take up the flux. The hammer should be of brass or other non-magnetic metal to prevent it from sticking to the magnetized steel. After the magnets are energized, they should be subjected to as few shocks or blows as possible, as this tends to weaken them.

YOUNGSTOWN, OHIO
E.D. GAGNIER

Recharging Permanent Magnets

MACHINERY MAGAZINE ENGINEERING ED – MARCH 1914

The December number of Machinery has just come to my desk, and if not too late I would like to offer an answer to A.B.'s inquiry in regard to a method of remagnetizing magneto generators – such as are used on automobile and motor cycle engines. These generators can be remagnetized by wrapping them with a temporary coil of from 30 to 60 turns of wire, and connecting this coil to a 110-volt direct-current circuit of considerable ampere capacity through a 10 or 15 ampere fuse and a knife switch. After the connections are made, the switch is closed, throwing the coil directly onto the line.

The fuse will be blown with some violence and the high current will force a heavy flux through the magnetic circuit and the armature. The armature, which is usually of the H-form, should be blocked in the position of least magnetic reluctance during this operation to provide for the minimum

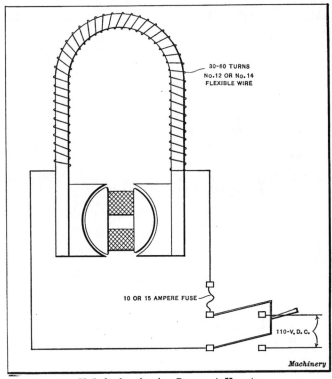

30-60 TURNS
No.12 OR No.14
FLEXIBLE WIRE

10 OR 15 AMPERE FUSE

110-V. D. C.

Machinery

Method of recharging Permanent Magnets

amount of magnetic flux cutting the armature winding. The proper position of the armature is shown in the diagram, which also illustrates the method of making the connections. No. 14 flexible wire and open link fuses will be found convenient and inexpensive, and a piece of sheet asbestos may be hung over the fuse to protect the workman's eyes from the flash. After the generator has been magne-tized, the coil should be removed, and if flexible wire is used the same coil may be employed over and over again. The advantage of this method is that it is not necessary to take the magneto apart or remove it from the machine. This also eliminates the possibility of replacing the magnets with the polarity reversed.

L.M.D.

Recharging Permanent Magnets

MACHINERY MAGAZINE ENGINEERING ED – MARCH 1914

In the December number of Machinery, A. B. asks how to recharge a permanent magnet. The following will be found a satisfactory method:

Attach the permanent magnet that is to be recharged to a direct-current electromagnet. Allow the two magnets to stay in this way for about 45 minutes and strike the permanent magnet light blows with a hammer every few minutes. The small particles of the steel which the chemist calls "molecules" must all lie in the same direction in order for the magnet to retain its magnetism. The light blows struck with the hammer while the current is flowing sets up a vibration in the steel which enables the molecules to adjust their position so that the magnetism is retained after the magnet to be charged is disconnected from the electromagnet.

GRAND RAPIDS, MICH.
GEORGE H. HAMILTON

Hardening Magnets

MACHINERY MAGAZINE – OCTOBER 21, 1915

H.L.W.– Our people have tried all ways to harden magneto magnets after they have been set to fit various pole cheeks, but without success. Some good information on the subject would be acceptable. Can any reader oblige?

Hardening Magnets

MACHINERY MAGAZINE – NOVEMBER 4, 1915

REPLY. – The accompanying rough sketch may be of some use to H.L.W., whose inquiry appeared on page 96 of your issue of October 21.

Hardening magnets is a difficult process, and after the most careful hardening they will require to be disc ground to fit the pole cheeks accurately. My experience has been that a pair of

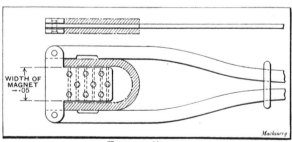

Hardening Magnets

tongs should be made as shown, the centre portion to be 0.05 inch less than the finished size of the magnet. This will give the magnet the required spring for a close fit.

As many holes as possible should be drilled in the centre of the tongs to allow the water to circulate freely. The magnet should be heated to 1000 deg. C., the tongs placed over the magnet in the furnace, and then plunged into a brine bath of about 100 deg. C. until cool (or until it can be touched with the hand). It is then allowed to cool off in the atmosphere.

N.G.

Permanent Magnets

MACHINERY MAGAZINE – NOVEMBER 16, 1916

F.N.C. – Can a reader tell me whether a permanent magnet should be dead hard, tempered, or soft in certain pertions? Also, what is the best method of re-magnetising same? The magnet I have is 1/4 inch x 1-1/2 inch in cross section, horse-shoe shape. I have tried a former coil on 230 volts which gives fair results, but the magnet is not so powerful as formerly.

Permanent Magnets

MACHINERY MAGAZINE – DECEMBER 14, 1916

A. – In reply to F.N.C.'s query on page 154, November 16th, 1916. Permanent magnets must be dead hard all over. A soft iron keeper should be carefully fitted to the poles since any air gap will diminish the magnetising effect considerably. A magnetising force of at least 50 ampere turns per centimeter length of the mean magnetic path must be applied.

Thus, if a current of 10 amperes is available, five turns of wire must be wound for each centimetre or, if the length of the magnetic path round the magnet and across the keeper is 50 cms., 5 x 50 turns of wire to carry 10 amperes must be wound on the magnet. If half this current is used, the number of turns must be doubled. The magnet may be tapped with a copper or wooden hammer while the current is "on." A resistance of about 23 ohms must be placed in series with the 230 volt supply as the resistance of the 250 turns of wire will be small.

W.D. Hills, B.Sc.

Hints on Magnet Making

by C. J. Webster

MACHINERY MAGAZINE – JANUARY 6, 1921

Horseshoe Magnets

Every care must be taken to use a first-class tungsten steel to ensure that the magnets will retain their magnetic power for long periods. Saw or shear the lengths off slightly longer than needed, and when heating prior to pressing into shape, use a muffle furnace with two ovens, the doors opening upwards. It is of great importance that a muffle be used as the heat from flames or gases affects tungsten steel and causes a skin to form. Preheat to 500 deg. C., and transfer to about 800 deg. C., press into shape, using a suitable screw press, such as a Rhodes, and use a gauge stop fitted on the die so that when pressed one leg is not longer than the other. While still hot place them edge upwards, with a distance piece between the legs, in a special vice called a flattener; screw them up and give them a couple of heavy blows. Place them in metal or iron boxes, as if they get cold too quickly trouble is caused when drilling. If, when pressed, they are

found to open too much they can be shaped up with a hammer till they fit the gauge required.

Grind the legs to the length wanted, after which place them in a jig on a small hand fly press fitted with a punch to dot them at the exact place where the holes

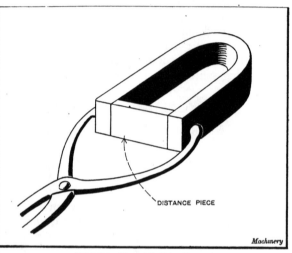

DISTANCE PIECE

Machinery

Horseshoe Magnet held by Tongs

need drilling; after drilling they are ready for hardening. This is by far the most important part of the procedure, and requires both experience and patience. Have a couple of furnaces placed side by side, and put a few magnets in the preheating chamber, which is maintained at 400 deg. C. When soaked, transfer to the other chamber at, say, 835-840 deg. C., which is an excellent temperature for magnet work. The hardener then quenches them in fresh cold water in a tank 3 feet deep and 4 feet long by 5 feet wide, with a baffle plate fixed about 6 inches from the far end, so that the fresh water will enter underneath about a foot below the surface. The water should be running slowly the whole time. A strong pair of tongs is needed as a firm grip is required. When quenching, place a distance piece of a size slightly under the gauge dimension required at the ends slightly under the gauge dimension required at the ends ads of the legs. The illustration shows the relative positions of the magnet, gauge and tongs. It is advisable, however, that the tongs have flanges of the full width of the magnet. If the legs open too much when hardened, use a slightly smaller distance piece, and vice versa.

The distance. piece used is simply a flat plate of about 1/4-inch in thickness and may, be of a width some 1-1/2-inches greater than the magnet width, as this allows the gauge to be gripped by the hand when in position between the magnet legs.

The magnets are withdrawn legs first from the furnace on to the front plate, the distance piece inserted and the magnet gripped, as shown, the edges of the distance piece being held by the thumb and forefinger of the left hand. The tongs must be very firmly gripped, as when the bow of the magnet enters the quench, there is a liability for the distance piece to spring out. When nearly quenched the grip is loosened and the gauge tried in the gap, any discrepancy

being rectified while the magnet is still under water.

Compass Magnets

During the war the writer had to harden millions of compass magnets from 1/16 by 1-1/2 inches up to 3/32 by 6 inches long. A good gas muffle furnace, 24 inches deep and natural draught, was used. The doors were removed and four fire tubes, 12 inches long and 3-3/4 inches in diameter obtained. Fire clay was rammed into one end of each of two of the tubes, and these were inserted at the bottom of the furnace with about 3 inches between them, the closed ends being at the rear. The other tubes were connected by sockets and these then projected by about 2 inches at the front of the furnace. In place of the doors the front was built up with fire brick and fire clay. A small brick wall was built in front to prevent the heat warming up the quenching tank, the top of which was 8 inches or so below the furnace plate.

A chute was fitted in front of the furnace and this, in turn, fitted the mouth of a sack that was held open and hung into the water in a V-shape, weights being used to keep the sack taut.

For supporting the magnets, plates curved to fit the furnace tubes were used, and the magnets laid side by side on these in single rows, and not one on top-of the other.

The plates are inserted and withdrawn with a pair of long thin tongs. While warming up prepare another plate, and when the first set of magnets is showing

39

a dull red, transfer these on their plate to the other and hotter tube which should heat them to about 840 deg. C. The tubes are thus used alternately. When the magnets are at quenching heat the plate is withdrawn and its corner tapped on the chute and the magnets jerked into the chute through the sack and into the quench. It is advisable to roll the magnets in a protecting powder before heating, as in this way they will remain bright after hardening.

Bar Magnets

Lengths should be cut slightly longer than required in the finished magnet to allow for grinding the ends square. The bars should be straightened by hammering on a hard wood block. Large sizes of bar magnets are best heated in an open-hearth fire using a saturated salt and water solution.

for quenching. For the small sizes use very small coke in the fire and impress the heated bits of a pair of tongs with a cold magnet, and when heating keep the tong bits red hot so that the magnets will be of a regular temperature throughout. When ready to quench grasp the bars in the centre with a pair of very narrow grip tongs, and plunge with a corkscrewing motion to prevent warpage. When nearly cold take out of the quenching solution and, if at all bent, strain straight as in file hardening. Use a small tank with a bar set across at about 8 inches from one end and a movable bar that can be clamped at a convenient distance from the fixed bar. Insert one end of the magnet between the bars, and strain gently with the left hand, spraying water from a jet held in the right hand.

Magnet Material

MACHINERY MAGAZINE – JULY 7, 1912

A.E.P. – What is the best material for magnets of the permanent horseshoe type? What is the smallest air gap that could be used without affecting the power of the magnet? What is the cheapest and best way to magnetize this type in large quantities?

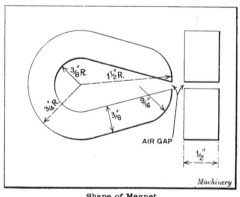

Shape of Magnet

Magnet Material

MACHINERY MAGAZINE – AUGUST 16, 1923

A.E.P. – What is the best material for magnets of the permanent horseshoe type ? What is the smallest air gap that could be used without affecting the power of the magnet ? What is the cheapest and best way to magnetize this type in large quantities ?

(Answered by P.W.P.)

The best and only materials for permanent magnets are the carbon and alloy crucible cast steels, more generally known as tool steels. These steels, free from defects and hardened and ground, give magnetic qualities and retentivity properties of high value.

Carbon steels having a carbon content 0.50 to 0.60 per cent. are employed where magnetic strength and retentivity are secondary considerations to the question of cost. In high grade magnets carbon and tungsten are generally considered by far the most important constituents. Manganese is found to reduce the capacity and should not be higher than 0.2 per cent. Silicon in small quantities is not detrimental, and sulphur and phosphorus have no influence on the capacity or permanence of magnet steels. Copper and nickel are found to be detrimental and should be definitely excluded. Molybdenum may be used instead of tungsten, and chromium has, until recently, been considered as inferior in its effect. During the last few years considerable research has been made in connection with high-grade magnet steels for magneto construction, in which the notable element or elements are cobalt or chrome and cobalt. These alloys are characterized by exceptionally high values of coercive force and satisfactory values of remanent flux-density and other magnetic constants, and are capable of withstanding vibration, shock, and rough usage.

On account of the scarcity of tungsten during the war, experiments were conducted in Germany with the object of finding a chromium-steel alloy which would prove suitable as a magnet steel in place of tungsten steel. Steel containing chromium 6 per cent. and carbon 1.1 per cent., hardened at 900 deg. C., gave the highest values. It was found that remanence decreases up. to 6 per cent. chromium as the quenching temperature rises, but that the coercive force diminishes. The carbon percentage varies the rate of increase or diminution of these values Alloys of the above composition having particular regard to coercive force, remanence, temperature coefficient and conservation of magnetism under shock and vibration, are highly suitable for permanent magnets and may be used as a substitute for tungsten steel. Typical permanent magnet steel analyses are given in the appended table:

COMPOSITION OF TYPICAL MAGNET STEELS

Authority.	Carbon.	Tungsten.	Chromium.	Cobalt.	Hardening Temperature.
Honda (Japan)	0.4 to 0.8	5.0 to 9.0	1.5 to 3.0	30.0 to 40.0	950 deg. C.
Gumlich (Germany)	1.13	—	6.0	—	900 deg. C.
Typical tungsten steels	0.62	5.7	Si 0.09	Mn 0.55	875 deg. C.
	0.60	5.37	Si 0.25	Mn 0.18	850 deg. C.

The coercive force in Honda's cobalt-tungsten-chrome steel varies from 215 to 257, approximately three times that of the best tungsten steel.

In connection with Gumlich's experiments with carbon-chromium steels as a substitute for tungsten steel, the analysis given in the table gave highest values for remanence X coercive force X 103=666. According to a paper read by W. Brown before the Royal Dublin Society in 1920, it would appear the chromium steels are less susceptible to decay or loss of magnetism. A number of magnets which had been laid aside for ten years, which were of varying composition, were tested for magnetic moment per gramme. The most retentive were found to be magnets with approximately 1 per cent. of carbon and 3 per cent. of chromium. The manganese group lost some 25 per cent. and the tungsten group approximately 20 per cent. of their magnetism.

Unless A.E.P. is in a position to conduct experiments concerning the most suitable steel for his particular purpose, it is advisable for him to rely upon the recommendations of one of the several reliable firms who specialize in the development and manufacture of this class of steel. In this connection the proposed specifications for permanent magnet steels suggested by Prof. Crapper, of the Electrical Engineering Department of Sheffield University, may be useful, and is as follows :

(1) Ordinary grade permanent magnet steel.

Coercive force, $H_c = 58$ C.G.S. units.

Remanent flux-density, $B_r = 10,000$.

Coefficient of retentivity, $c = \dfrac{B_r}{B_{i\,max}} = 0.65$.

The product, $H_c \times c = 40$.

Magnetic strength, $H_c \times B_r = 560,000$.

Specific reluctivity at the remanence point, $\dfrac{H_c}{I_r} = 0.07$.

Available external magnetic energy $(\beta\phi)$ max $= 240,000$.

(2) Higher grade magneto magnet steel.

Coercive force, $H_c = 65$ C.G.S. units.

Remanent intensity, $I_r = 760$.

Coefficient of retentivity, $c = \dfrac{B_r}{B_{i\,max}} = 0.7$.

The product, $H_c \times c = 50$.

Magnetic strength, $H_c \times B_r = 600,000$.

Specific reluctivity at the remanence point $\dfrac{H_c}{I_r} = 0.085$.

Available external magnetic energy $(\beta\phi)$ max $= 300,000$.

(3) Special grades of permanent magnet steel.

Coercive force, $H_c = 200$ C.G.S. units.

Remanent intensity, $I_r = 800$.

Coefficient of retentivity, $c = \dfrac{B_r}{B_{i\,max}} = 0.625$.

The product, $H_c \times c = 125$.

Magnetic strength, $H_c \times B_r = 2,000,000$.

Specific reluctivity at remanence point, $\dfrac{H_c}{I_r} = 0.25$.

Available external magnetic energy $(\beta\phi)$ max $= 600,000$ to 1,000,000.

The question of the smallest air gap which may be used in the magnet shown depends upon questions of relation between magnetic hysteresis and coercive force, and other highly technical factors which to-day form the basis of considerable discussion between electrical experts. There is also the consideration of the actual circumstances under which the magnet will function and the determination of the most suitable gap will probably be ascertained quickly and economically by actual experiment under working conditions.

The process of magnetizing is a simple and quick one. The solenoid method is the most satisfactory and provided the air gap provides sufficient clearance for the solenoids, magnetizing may be effected in approximately half a minute.

reprinted from
Principles of Physics
or Natural Philosophy
by Benjamin Silliman, Jr., M.A., M.D.
Second Edition – 1865

CHAPTER III.

ELECTRICITY.

773. General statement.—Electricity is conveniently subdivided into, 1. Magnetic electricity or magnetism; 2. Statical or frictional electricity; and, 3. Dynamical or Voltaic electricity. We will consider the subject in this order.

§ 1. Magnetic Electricity.

I. PROPERTIES OF MAGNETS.

774. Lodestone—natural magnets.—There is found in nature an ore of iron, called by mineralogists *magnetite*, or magnetic iron, some specimens of which possess the power of attracting to themselves small fragments of a like kind, or of metallic iron. This power has been called *magnetism*, from the name of the ancient city of Magnesia, in Lydia (Asia Minor), near which the ore spoken of was first found. It crystallizes in forms of the monometric system, often modified octohedra, like fig. 520, and is a compound of one equivalent of peroxyd of iron with one of protoxyd. ($FeO + Fe_2O_3$ = Fe_3O_4.) It is one of the best ores of this valuable metal.

520

Formerly all magnets were lodestones, or natural magnets. A fragment of this ore rolled in iron filings or magnetic sand, becomes tufted, as in fig. 521, not alike in all parts, but chiefly at the ends. Fig. 522 shows a similar mass mounted in a frame, ll, with poles, pp', of soft iron. Thus mounted, the lodestone gains in strength, by sustaining a weight from the hook below, on a soft iron cross-bar.

521   522

775. Artificial magnets are made by touch or influence from a lodestone, or from another magnet, or by an electrical current. Hardened steel is found to retain this influence permanently, while masses of soft iron become magnets only when in contact with, or within a certain distance of a permanent magnet. Artificial magnets are more powerful than the lodestone, and possess properties entirely identical with it. Magnets attract at all distances, but their power increases, like all forces acting from a centre, inversely as the square of the distance. Heat diminishes the power of magnets, but if not heated beyond a certain degree (full redness), this power returns on cooling, and is increased at lower temperatures. Above that point, the coercitive force is destroyed, and they lose all magnetic power.

Various forms are given to magnets. The *bar magnet* is a simple straight bar of hardened steel. If curved so as to bring the ends near together, it is called a *horse shoe* magnet, and if several bars, straight or curved, are bound together into one, fig. 523, it is called a compound magnet, or magnetic battery. The

523

most powerful artificial magnets can sustain only about twenty-eight or thirty times their own weight. Usually they sustain very much less than this.

Magnetic needles are light bars, fig. 524, suspended on a central point so as to move in obedience to terrestrial or artificial attractions. The mode of making magnets, and the circumstances influencing their power, are noticed hereafter.

524

776. **Distribution of the magnetic force—polarity.**—The magnetic force is not equally distributed in all parts of a magnet, but is found concentrated chiefly about the ends, and diminishing toward the centre, which is neutral. The points of greatest attraction are called *poles*. When a magnet is rolled in iron filings or magnetic sand, the position of the poles is seen as in the bar magnet, fig. 525,

525

whose centre is found to be quite devoid of the attracted particles which cluster about the ends. The point of no attraction is called the neutral point—line of magnetic indifference, or equator of magnetism. Every magnet has at least two poles, and one neutral point. The magnetic poles are distinguished as N or S, Austral or Boreal (A and B), or by the signs, plus (+) and minus (—), all these signs having reference to the earth's attraction, and to the antagonism between the poles of unlike name. The law regulating the distribution of magnetic force in a bar, was determined by Coulomb, by means of the torsion balance, § 820, to be very nearly as the squares of the distance of any given point, from the magnetic equator or neutral point.

777. **Magnetic phantom—magnetic curves.**—The distribution of the magnetic force about the poles of a magnet is beautifully shown by placing a sheet of stiff paper over the poles of a horse-shoe magnet, and scattering fine iron filings or magnetic sand from a sieve or gauze bag over the paper. As they touch the surface of the paper, each filing assumes a certain position, marking the exact place of the magnetic poles and of the neutral line, as seen in fig. 526. The magnet may be laid horizontally, or a series of magnetic bars may be placed as in fig. 532, producing very pleasing and instructive results. Tapping

526

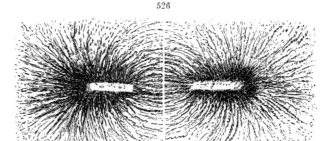

the edge of the paper gently with the nail, or a pen-stick, facilitates the adjustment of the filings. The curves exhibited by the magnetic phantom have been mathematically investigated by De Haldat, who for that purpose transferred them to a glued paper.

To fix the curves, Nicklés uses a waxed paper, and when the figures are produced, they may be fixed in position by holding a heated plate of iron near the surface of the paper. As soon as the wax is fused, which is easily perceived by its shining appearance, the source of heat is withdrawn, and as the wax cools the filings become fixed in position and in full relief. (Am. Jour. Sci [2] XXX. 62.) The curves may then be more conveniently studied.

778. **Magnetic figures** may be produced on the surface of a thin steel plate, by marking on it with one pole of a bar magnet. Magnetism is thus produced in the steel along the line of contact, which is afterwards made evident by magnetic sand, or iron filings sprinkled on the plate. These lines may be varied or multiplied at pleasure, with pleasing effects; their polarity is always the reverse of that carried by the bar. They may be made even through paper or card-board, and will remain for a long time. Blows, or heat, will remove them. Hard

plate steel is best for this purpose, about one-twentieth to one-eighth of an inch thick, and six inches to twelve inches square.

779. **Anomalous magnets** are such as have more than *two* poles. Thus the bar seen in fig. 527 has a pair of similar poles (—), at the centre, and its ends are con- sequently similar (+), while it has two neutral points at *a* and *c*. Fig. 528 shows a bar with three sets of poles, arranged

527

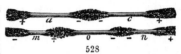

528

alternately — and +, with three neutral points at *m*, *o*, and *n*. Broken at these neutral points, every magnet becomes two or more separate magnets, with corresponding polarity.

780. **Attraction and repulsion.**—The law of magnetic attraction and repulsion is, that *like poles repel, and unlike poles attract each other.*

If a piece of soft iron is presented to either pole of a magnetic needle, fig. 524, there is attraction, which is reciprocal between the needle and the iron; for if the iron is suspended, and the needle approached to it, the iron is attracted by either end of the needle. If, however, a magnet is approached to the needle, + to —, there is attraction; if — to — or + to +, there is repulsion.

If the unlike poles of two equal magnetic bars, tufted with iron filings, are approached, the tufts join in a festoon; but if the poles are of the same name, most of the filings fall. For the same reason, if a magnetic bar, B, fig. 529, is

529

slid upon another bar, A, of equal power to B, as the two opposite ends approach each other, the key, previously suspended, falls, because the two bars mutually neutralize each other by the opposing action of the austral and boreal magnetism.

. 781. **Magnetism by contact.**—When a mass of iron, or of any magnetizable body, is placed in contact with a magnet, it receives magnetism throughout its mass, and of the same name as the pole with which it is in contact. Thus, in fig. 530, the soft iron key is sustained by the north pole of a magnetic bar; a second key, a nail, a tack, and some iron filings, are, in succession, also sustained by the magnetism imparted by contact from the bar magnet through the soft iron. The series of soft iron rings, in fig. 531, is sustained from the bar magnet under the same conditions of polarity. Tested by a delicate needle.

every part of the sustained masses will manifest only north polarity, and we may regard them as only prolongations of the original pole. This is analogous to electrical conduction.

530

Pure soft iron receives magnetism sooner and more powerfully than steel or cast iron, and also parts with it sooner. Hardened steel and hard cast iron retain more or less of the magnetic force permanently. No other metals beside iron, nickel, cobalt, and possibly manganese, can receive and retain magnetism by contact.

531

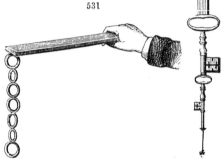

These are, therefore, called the magnetic metals.

782. **Magnetism in bodies not ferruginous.**—Beside the magnetic metals, so called, Cavallo has shown that the alloy, brass, becomes magnetic (slightly) by hammering, but loses that property again by heat. Some minerals are magnetic, particularly when they have been heated. The pure earths, and even silica, are found to have the same property. In the case of silica, and some other minerals containing oxyd of iron in combination, this is not so surprising. M. Biot determined in the case of two specimens of mica, one from Siberia (muscovite), and the other from Zinnwald (lithia mica), that their magnetic powers were (by the method of oscillations) as 6·8 to 20, and he remarked, if the oxyd of iron be the cause of their magnetic virtue, it should exist in the minerals in the above proportion ; and curiously enough, the result of Vauquelin's analyses (then unknown to M. Biot) corresponded, almost exactly, to these numbers.

Some states of chemical combination, however, appear to destroy, or cloak, the magnetic virtues of iron; e. g. an alloy of iron, one part, with antimony four parts, was found by Seebeck to be utterly devoid of magnetic action ; and the magnetic power of nickel is entirely concealed in the alloy called German silver.

The researches of Faraday have shown matter of all kinds to be subject to a certain modified degree of influence by magnetism (§ 799. *Diamagnetism*).

II. MAGNETIC INDUCTION OR INFLUENCE.

783. **Induction.**—Every magnet is surrounded by a sphere of magnetic influence, which has been called its magnetic atmosphere. Every magnetizable substance within this influence becomes magnetic also (without contact), the parts contiguous to the magnet pole, having an

46

opposite, and those remote from it, a similar name. This influence is called *induction*.

Thus, in fig. 532, the north end of a bar magnet induces south polarity in the contiguous ends of the five bars surrounding it, and north polarity in their remote ends. If these bars are of hardened steel, they 532 will retain a small portion of the magnetic force induced from a powerful bar, but if they are of soft iron, they will part with their magnetism as soon as the source of excitation is withdrawn. In this case, the magnetized bars have a tendency to move up to the magnet, and are prevented from doing so only by friction and gravity. The attraction is reciprocal, and we hence infer that there is induction in every case of magnetic attraction.

In the iron filings, arranged in magnetic curves, fig. 526, on a glass plate, or card-board, the same tendency is observed.

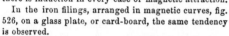

Small pieces of soft iron wire suspended from the ends of a thread near, and parallel to each other, when approached by a bar magnet, receive induced magnetism, the farther ends diverging by mutual repulsion. Two sewing-needles thus suspended and influenced, become permanent magnets.

The ingenuity of the teacher will furnish many pleasing and instructive illustrations of magnetic induction.

784. Theoretical considerations.—The real nature of the magnetic force is unknown to us; but the analogies offered by electro-magnetism and magneto-electricity, lead to the conviction that it is one mode of electrical excitement. Unlike light, heat, and statical electricity, magnetism affords no phenomena immediately addressed to the senses. It is distinguished from statical electricity chiefly by its permanent character when once excited, and by the very limited number of substances capable of receiving and manifesting it.

785. Theory of two fluids.—It may be assumed that there are two magnetic or electrical fluids (the Boreal or positive, and the Austral or negative), which are in a state of equilibrium or combination in all bodies; that in iron, nickel, &c., these two forces are capable of separation, by virtue of the inductive influence of the earth, or of another magnet, while, in other bodies, this permanent separation cannot be effected. The two magnetic forces are never seen isolated from each other, but are always united in one bar. Hence, we cannot have a boreal magnet, or an austral magnet, as we may in statical electricity produce, at pleasure, vitreous or resinous excitement over the whole surface of a body. Both poles must coexist in every magnet. If we break a magnetic bar at its neutral point, we have two magnets of diminished force, but each half has its two poles like the original bar, and its neutral point also. The *anomalous* magnets, figs. 527, 528, will render this statement intelligible. Every magnet must, in this view, be regarded as an assemblage of numberless small magnets, every molecule of steel having its own poles antagonistic to those of the next contiguous particle. This conception is rendered clearer to the senses by fig. 533. Here the N and S poles of the several particles are each re-presented as pointing one way re-spectively, and towards the N and S ends of the bar.

These opposing forces, therefore, constantly increase from the centre or neutral point, where they are in equilibrium, to the ends, where they find their maximum. This arbitrary illustration enables us to conceive how such a body may excite similar manifesta-tions of power in another, without itself being weakened, and how each part becomes a perfect magnet, if the bar is broken. The experi-ment shown in fig. 529, illustrates well the reunion of the two fluids, to form the neutral state of the undecomposed influence.

De Haldat has shown that a brass tube, filled with iron filings, confined by screwed caps of brass, can be magnetized by any of the modes used for bars, and have its poles and neutral point like a bar magnet; but if, by concussion, the particles of iron are disarranged, the magnetic force diminishes, and finally disappears.

The magnetic pastes of Dr. Knight and of Ingenhausz, also illustrate the fact, that little particles of magnetic iron, or of pulverized lodestone, may determine the existence of the magnetic poles, and a neutral line, when they are compacted into a mass, by drying oils, or by the use of some gummy substance.

Even so small a quantity as one-sixth of ferruginous particles, in five-sixths of sand or earthy matter, can be magnetized as a bar, showing clearly the de-composition of the neutral fluid in each particle.

786. **Coercitive force.**—The resistance which most substances show to the induction of magnetism, has been distinguished by the term *co-ercitive force*. In soft iron, this force may be regarded as at a minimum, since this substance will receive magnetic influence even from being placed in the line of magnetic dip, while in steel which has been hard-ened, a peculiar manipulation is required to induce any permanent magnetism. Soft iron parts with its induced magnetism as readily as it receives it; but, if it is hardened by blows, or violent twisting, or by small portions of phosphorus, arsenic, or carbon combined with it, a portion of magnetism is permanently retained by it from induction.

As blows, by hardening, may induce permanent magnetism in soft iron, so, in steel, the coercitive force may, by simple vibration, as by blows on a magnetic bar, or by an accidental fall, destroy a large part of the force developed, by giving opportunity to the coercitive force to resume its supremacy. In general, whatever cause induces hardness, increases the coercitive force; and, conversely, it is diminished by annealing, or any cause which results in softening the mass.

III. TERRESTRIAL MAGNETISM.

787. **Magnetic needle.—Directive tendency.**—A magnetic nee-

dle, suspended over the poles of a horse-shoe magnet, comes to rest in the plane of the poles; and, in obedience to the fundamental law of magnetic attractions, its A and B poles will be opposite to the B and A poles of the attracting magnet. The suspended needle, in fig. 534, assumes its position by reason of the same law, and comes to rest with its A pole toward the N pole of the earth, and its B pole towards the south. All bar magnets, having a free motion in a horizontal plane, arrange themselves in this manner in every part of the earth.

534

This directive tendency of the magnet has been known to European nations since the twelfth century; but was known, it is said, to the Chinese, 2000 B. C. The earliest mariner's compass, used by Syrian navigators in 1242, was a common sewing-needle, rendered magnetic, thrust through a reed or cork, and allowed to float on water. (Klaproth.) This directive power renders the compass invaluable to the explorer of a pathless wilderness, to the surveyor and the miner; the mineralogist and the physicist also find it indispensable in many researches.

The terms *Austral* and *Boreal* have been applied to the polarity of the magnetic needle, in allusion to the free Austral and Boreal magnetism assumed to exist respectively in the southern and northern regions of the earth. In accordance with magnetic law, the end of the needle pointing north is called *Austral*, and that pointing south, *Boreal*. For greater simplicity, the mariner's compass is marked N on that point which turns to the north, and conversely; but the terms austral and boreal may be used interchangeably with positive and negative, or north and south polarity.

The mariner's compass is arranged in a box (K, fig. 535) called a

535   536

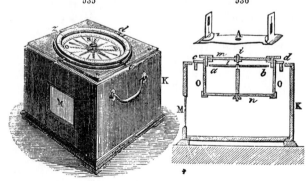

binnacle, illuminated at night through the glass, M. The magnetic needle, *a b*, fig. 536, delicately poised on a socket of agate, is attached to the lower side of a card or plate of mica, *t*, on which is printed the star of thirty-two points,—seven between each two of the cardinal points, N., E., S., and W. The compass-box, *o o*, is hung on points called gimbals, *c d c z* (pronounced *gimbles*), which allow it to remain always horizontal, however the ship may roll. The transom or cross-sights, A, may be placed at pleasure on the face, *m*, of the compass, when the object is to measure points on the coast. Both parts of the figure are similarly lettered.

The astatic needle is an instrument in which the directive tendency of the earth's magnetism is neutralized, by placing two equal needles, *a b*, *b' a'*, fig. 537, parallel, one above the other, with their unlike poles opposed to each other. This system is suspended by a fibre of raw silk, and is a most sensitive test for feeble magnetic currents. Such is the construction adopted in the galvani-scope, to be hereafter described. The two needles must be of exactly equal force, or *a b* and *a' b'* will not neutralize each other, and the system will have a directive tendency, equal to any difference of force in the two needles.

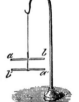

537

The most simple astatic needle is made by touching a steel sewing-needle, at its centre of weight, by the N. pole of a powerful magnet; the point touched develops two S. poles, and the two ends are N. Such a needle is very nearly astatic.

788. **Magnetic meridian—declination or variation.**—There are but few places in the world where the magnetic needle points to the true, or astronomical North; and in all other places, a plane passing through the axis of the magnetic needle (the magnetic meridian), fails to coincide with the geographical meridian. Moreover, the magnetic meridian in any given place is not constant, but changes slowly from year to year (called *secular variation*), being now on the E., and again on the W. side of the true North. This is called the *declination* or *variation* of the magnetic needle. The declination is called Eastern, or Western, according as it may be to the East or to the West of the astronomical meridian. The angle formed by the meeting of the true and the magnetic meridians is called the *angle of declination*. Thus, at Washington City,* the angle of declination in 1855–6, was 2° 36′ W., and at New Haven it was 6° 37′·9 W., August 12, 1848. Js. Ruth, observer.

Columbus, in his first voyage to America, found the needle to have, as he sailed westwards, an increasing variation from the true North, a circumstance not before observed, and which caused the greatest consternation in his super-stitious crew, "who thought the laws of nature were changing, and that the compass was about to lose its mysterious power." (Irving's Columbus.) Not-

---

* U. S. Coast Survey Report, 1858, 196. C. A. Schott, Observer.

46 *

withstanding these and other similar observations, it was not until the middle of the seventeenth century, that the variation of the compass was an established fact in magnetic science. The observations on the declination cf the compass in England, date from 1580. The following table, from Harris, contains the declination with the mean rate of motion, as referred to certain periods of observation in London, between 1580 and 1850, or about two hundred and seventy years. Eastern declination being distinguished by the negative sign, and western by the positive sign.

	Eastern Declination.		Zero.				Western Declination.		
Years,	1580.	1622.	1660.	1692.	1730.	1765	1818	1850
Declination,	—11° 15′	—6°	0	+6°	+13°	+20°	+24° 41′	+22° 30′
Rate per year,	7′	8′	10′	11′	11′·5	9′	0′	5′

Thus, in a period of eighty years from the first observation, the needle gradually reached the true meridian, and then, for a period of one hundred and fifty-eight years, it moved Westward, reaching its maximum Westerly declination in 1818, and it is now again slowly moving Eastwards. The rate of this movement is not uniform, but is greater near the minimum, and least near the maximum, point of declination.

Observations since 1700 establish the same facts in the United States, at a great number of places. Thus, at Burlington, Vt., in 1790, the declination was $+7°·8$; in 1830, $+8°·30$; in 1840, $+9°\ 07$; and, in 1860, $+10°·30$. In Cambridge, Mass., in 1700, it was $+9°·9$, and steadily diminished to 1790, when it was $+6°·9$, and has since regularly increased to the present time, being, in 1855, $+10°·90$. At Hatborough, Pa., in A. D. 1680, the declination was $+8°·5$; in 1800 it had, by a regular rate, decreased to $+1°·8$, and, in 1860, was $+5°·32$. At Washington, D. C., it was $+0·6$ in A. D. 1800, and in 1860 had increased to $+2°·9$.

South of Washington, the declination is uniformly Easterly, ranging, at Charleston, S. C., from $—3°·7$ in A. D. 1770, to $—1°·7$ in 1860. On the Western Coast of North America, it is also Easterly; being, for example, at San Francisco, in 1790, $—13°·6$, and in 1860, $—15·°8$. The annual change (increasing E. declination) being, in 1840, $—1′·6$; in 1850, $—1′·2$; and in 1860, $—0′·8$.

For a full discussion of Magnetic Declination in the United States, the student will refer to the Reports of the United States Coast Survey; and for an able extract of all the results of secular change on the Atlantic, Gulf, and Pacific Coasts of the United States, refer to a "Report by Assistant Charles A. Schott," in Am. Jour. Sci. [2] XXIX., p. 335.

The first attempt to systematize the variations of the magnetic needle, and to connect by lines, called *isogonic* lines, all those places on the earth where the declination was similar, was made by Halley, about 1700. He thus discovered two distinct lines of no inclination, called *agonic* lines, one of which ran obliquely over North America and across the Atlantic Ocean, and another descended through the middle of China and across New Holland; and he inferred that these lines communicated near both poles of the earth.

789. **Variation chart.—Isogonal lines.**—In fig. 538, is seen a projection of the lines of equal and no declination, on a Mercator's chart of the earth, embracing observations down to 1835. The Ameri-

can line of no variation, or *agone*, crosses the eastern point of South America, in latitude 20° S., skirts the Windward Antilles, enters North

538

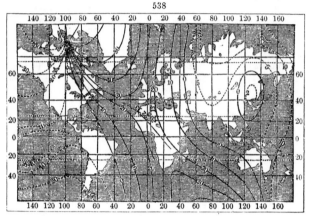

Carolina near Cape Lookout, and passing through Staunton, in Virginia, crosses Lake Erie midway on its course to Hudson's Bay. The chief Asiatic agone (for, in fact, there are two lines of no variation), after traversing the Indian Ocean in a southerly direction, crosses the western part of New Holland near 120° E. All the entire lines on this chart indicate western declination, while the dotted lines mark eastern declination. According to the theory of Gauss, the eminent German astronomer, no lines of equal variation can form diverging branches, or be tangents to each other; but when there is a space within which the declination is less than outside any portion of its limiting line, that line must form a loop, the two branches intersecting at right angles. The observed line of 8° 40′ in the Pacific, beautifully illustrates and confirms this theoretical position, as shown on the chart, fig. 538.

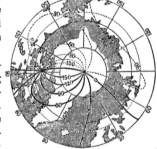

539

Figure 539 illustrates the circumpolar relations of the corresponding lines of equal variation in the northern hemisphere. It will be seen that much the larger number of the isogonal lines, converge on the Mercator's projection at a point near Baffin's Bay, in lat. 73°·0 N., long. 70°·0 W., its opposite pole is to the southward of New Holland.

Halley's original chart assumes the existence of two magnetic poles in each hemisphere, one fixed, and the other revolving about it in a certain period. Hansteen, in 1828, in his well-known chart, accepts the same view. By Gauss's theory of terrestrial magnetism, only one magnetic pole in each hemisphere is required, and thus far observation has shown a wonderful conformity between the theory of Gauss and the facts.

790. **Daily variations of the magnetic needle.**—Besides the great secular movements of the magnetic needle already noticed (788), it is found to vary sensibly from day to day, and even with the different periods of the same day. The most refined means have been in our time applied to the exact investigation of this phenomenon, first noticed by Graham, a London optician, in 1722. It has been shown that the north pole of the needle begins between seven and eight A. M. to move westward, and this movement continues until one P. M., when it becomes stationary. Soon after one o'clock it slowly returns eastward, and at about ten P. M., the needle again becomes stationary at the point from which it started. During the night, a small oscillation occurs, the north pole moving west until three A. M., and returning again as before. The mean daily change, as observed by Capt. Beaufoy, is not quite one degree. This daily disturbance of the magnetic needle is undoubtedly due to the action of the sun, and it will therefore vary in different latitudes. In the Southern hemisphere, the daily oscillations are of course reversed in direction to those of the Northern hemisphere.

The annual variation of the needle was discovered by Cassini, in 1786. We have, therefore, 1st, the great *secular variations*, continued through long periods of time; 2d, *annual variations*, conforming to the movement of the sun in the solstices; 3d, *daily variations*, conforming nearly to the periods of maximum and minimum temperature in each day, and lastly, *irregular variations*, connected with the aurora borealis, or other cosmical phenomena, which Humboldt has called *magnetic storms*.

791. **Dip or inclination.**—A needle, hung as in fig. 540, within a stirrup upon the points *a b*, the whole system being suspended by a thread, will, before magnetizing, if carefully adjusted, stand in any position in which it may be placed. If now the needle be magnetized, it forthwith assumes the position seen in the figure, its pole dipping toward the North pole of the earth. In this latitude (41° 18′), the dip was, in 1848, 73° 31′·9. Such a needle is called a *dipping needle*, and if constructed as in the figure, it shows both the declination and dip, or inclination, of terrestrial magnetism for any given locality. As the whole system is free to move, it will obviously arrange itself in the magnetic meridian, and its position of equilibrium will be the resultant of the two forces of declination and dip. Approaching the equator, the dipping needle becomes constantly less and less inclined, until at

last a point is found where it is quite horizontal, and this point will be in the *magnetic equator;* an imaginary plane near, but not coincident with, the equator of the earth.

540

The discovery of the magnetic dip or inclination, was made in 1576, by Robert Norman, a practical optician of London, who constructed the first dipping needle, by which he determined the dip at London at that time to be nearly 72°. The magnetic dip, like the declination, is subject to continual and progressive changes, both secular and periodical, and it is at this moment rapidly decreasing. Thus at London in 1576 it was 71° 50', in 1676 it had become 73° 30', and in 1723 it was 74° 42', having then reached its maximum. In 1790 it had decreased to 71° 3', and in 1800 to 70° 35'. Sabine, in 1821, fixed it at 70° 3', and Kater, in 1830, at 69° 88'. It is now, in England, about 68° 30', having decreased in 128 years about 6° 12', or at the rate of nearly 3' yearly, the mean annual movement from 1830 to 1850 being at the rate of more than 4' yearly, while between 1723 and 1790 it was about 2 5' yearly, showing an accelerated and retarded movement in the secular changes of the dipping needle, or magnetic inclination.

792. **The action of the earth's magnetism** on the dipping needle is neatly illustrated by the simple arrangement seen in fig. 541, where the magnetic bar *s n*, is placed horizontally on the diameter of a semicircle, representing an arc of the meridian, on which a small dipping needle is made to occupy successively the position seen at *a, a', a'', a'''.*

541

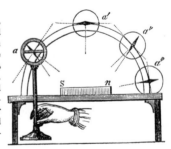

At *a'*, the needle is horizontal, being at the magnetic equator, and equally acted on by both poles. In every other position, the influence of one pole must predominate, to a greater or less extent, over the other. Several sewing-needles, suspended over a magnetic bar at equal distances, one over each end, one over the centre, and one intermediate, will illustrate the same point satisfactorily.

793. **Dipping needle.**—The dipping needle of Biot, shown in fig. 542, is wholly of brass, and embraces two graduated circles, *m* and M, one horizontal and one vertical. The circle, M, with its supporting frame, A, moves in azimuth over *m*, by which it is placed in the magnetic meridian. It is leveled by the level, *n*, adjusted by three

milled heads in the feet. The needle, *a b*, is suspended on the bars, *r*. To fix the magnetic meridian by this instrument, the circle, *m*, is

revolved until the needle, *a b*, stands vertical and points to 90°, it is then in the magnetic equator, a position of course exactly 90° from the magnetic meridian, which is then obtained by revolving the frame, A, 90° backwards. The angle, *a c d*, is the angle of inclination (or dip), and is read on the arc M.

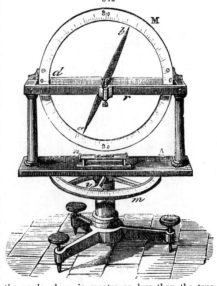

542

Two small errors of observation exist in this instrument; 1st, from the fact that the magnetic axis of the needle does not coincide with the axis of its form, and 2d, from the circumstance that the centre of gravity of the needle does not lie in the points of suspension, and that therefore the angle, *d c a*, is greater or less than the true angle of inclination, by a very small quantity. The first is corrected by reversing the plane of the instrument, by a revolution of 180°, and taking the mean of the two readings; the second, by reversing the polarity of the needle by touch on the opposite poles of two bar magnets, provided for the purpose. By this means, the centre of gravity is brought, first above, and then below the point of suspension, and the mean of the two readings is the true angle sought.

794. **Inclination map, or isoclinal lines.**—In fig. 543, is presented a Mercator's projection of the line of no dip, or magnetic equator, and the position of the isoclinal lines of 30°, 50°, 70°, 80°, and 85° north, and 30°, 50°, and 70° south. It will be noticed that the magnetic is below the terrestrial equator, in all the western hemisphere, and is above it in the eastern, crossing it near the island of St. Thomas, in longitude 3° E., and again in the Pacific ocean. These points of intersection of course vary with the progressive changes of the magnetic dip. The greatest declination of the magnetic equator from the equinoctial line, amounts to about 20° N., near 53° E. longitude, and its greatest southern declination is 13°, in about 40° W. longitude, near the bay of Bahia, on the East coast of South America.

The inclination of the needle at any place is, approximately, twice its magnetic latitude. (Kraft.)

543

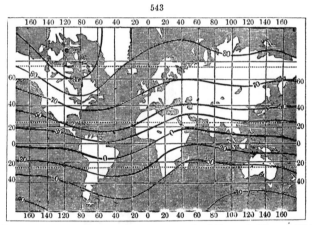

Figure 544 shows the relation of the isoclinal lines of 80° and 85° in the northern hemisphere, to the lines of latitude, and to the N. magnetic pole, near Baffin's Bay. Sir James Ross, in 1832, found the needle to dip near Prince Regent's Inlet, lat. 70° N., longitude 96° N., within one minute of 90°.

544

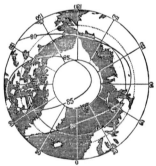

It is to be observed, that the lines of equal magnetic inclination (isoclinal lines), are found to approach in position, with very considerable conformity, to the isothermal lines, or lines of equal temperature, thus indicating a close relation between the earth's magnetism and the distribution of the terrestrial heat.

795. **Magnetic intensity.**—It is plain, from the phenomena of the magnetic declination and dip already considered, that the distribution of magnetic force over the earth is unequal, although in general it is most active about the poles, and least so about the equator. The question arises, how may the magnetic intensity at any given point of the earth be determined? This question is answered by the use of the *needle of oscillation.* A large number of facts serve to show, that a freely suspended needle in a state of oscillation, is influenced by the

magnetic force of the earth, in a way analogous to that of a common pendulum, oscillating by the influence of gravity; and that hence by means of such a needle, we may determine the ratio of the intensity of terrestrial magnetic force throughout the whole extent of the earth's surface.

This mode of determining the magnetic intensity in different regions of the earth, was first suggested by Graham, in 1775, and was afterwards more fully perfected and employed by Coulomb, Humboldt, Hansteen, and Gauss. Humboldt carefully determined the time of a given number of oscillations of a small magnetic needle, first at Paris, and afterward in Peru. At Paris, the needle made two hundred and forty-five oscillations in ten minutes: in Peru, it made only two hundred and eleven in the same time. The relative intensities were therefore as the square of these two numbers, or as 1 : 1·3482, which, assuming the point on the magnetic equator in Peru as unity, will give the magnetic intensity at Paris as 1·3482. This kind of observation has since been extended to nearly every known part of the globe, and full tables have been published, giving the results. Thus the intensity at Rio de Janeiro is 0·887; Cape of Good Hope, 0·945; Peru, 1·; Naples, 1·274; Paris, 1·348; Berlin, 1·364; London, 1·369; St. Petersburg, 1·403; Baffin's Bay, 1·707.

The most complete statement of the results of American observations on the magnetic elements has lately been published by Dr. A. D. Bache, in Am. Jour. Sci. [2] XXIV., p. 1, where all the earlier observations are collated, with the more extended results of the Coast Survey, with maps.

796. **Isodynamic lines**, or lines of equal power, are such as connect places in which observations show the magnetic intensity to be equal. These lines are not always parallel to the isoclinal lines, although nearly so, and the points of greatest and least intensity are not exactly identical with the points of greatest and least inclination. Hence the intensity of the magnetic equator may not be everywhere the same. These lines are probably curves of double curvature returning into themselves, implying the existence of two intensity poles, the western, near Hudson's Bay, in lat. 50° N., lon. 90° W; and the eastern or Siberian pole, about 70° N., and lon. 120° E. The two southern poles have been placed, one to the south of New Holland, in lat. 60° S., lon. 140° E.; the other, in the South Pacific, also in lat. 60° S., but lon. 120° W. These four poles are not therefore diametrically opposite to each other.

The terrestrial magnetic force increases toward the south pole, nearly in the ratio of 1 : 3, and as both the maximum and minimum magnetic intensity on the globe are found in the southern hemisphere, it would appear that the ratio of 1 : 3 expresses very nearly the maximum and minimum magnetic force of the whole earth. From the profound inquiries of Gauss, it appears that the absolute terrestrial magnetic force, considering the earth as a magnet, is equal to six magnetic steel bars of a pound weight each, magnetized to saturation, for every cubic yard of surface. Compared with one such bar, the total magnetism of the earth is as 8,864,000,000,000,000,000,000 : 1, a most inconceivable proportion. (Harris.)

797. **The inductive power of the earth's magnetism** is manifested by the polarity developed in any bar of soft iron, or of steel, placed in an erect position, as in fig. 545, or better, in the angle of the dip of the place. The end of the bar toward the earth is always Austral, Boreal magnetism existing at the upper end, B, and a neutral point at the centre, M. These facts are demonstrated by the action of a small needle, held in the hand at the three positions, shown in the figure. If the experiment were made in the southern hemisphere, the polarity would be reversed.

545

For this reason, all masses of iron standing in a vertical position become magnetic. In soft iron this magnetism is transient, but in steel tools, especially such as are subject to vibration, as drills, the magnetism developed is permanent.

Barlow found that globes of iron, like bomb shells, a foot or more in diameter, become miniature copies of the earth by virtue of the inductive force exerted upon them by the earth's magnetism; having a magnetic axis in the line of dip at the place of experiment, and an equator at right angles to their axis. Delicate needles, poised on the equatorial line of such globes, suffered no disturbance, while in any other position on the sphere, both declination and dip were manifest.

Barlow further discovered, that such a sphere of iron, placed in a certain relation to a compass needle on board a ship, united, and harmonized the local attractions of the ship's iron, so as to free the compass from the effects of such disturbing causes.

798. **System of simultaneous magnetic observations.**—The distinguished Prussian philosopher, Alex. v. Humboldt, in 1836, proposed to the scientific world to set on foot a series of connected and simultaneous observations, to be made over as large a portion of the earth's surface as possible, for the purpose of establishing the laws relating to the magnetic forces.

In accordance with this suggestion, the leading governments of Europe (France excepted), and many of the scientific societies both in the old and new world, commenced such observations, with instruments specially contrived for the purpose, and in buildings made without iron, both on and beneath the earth's surface. Expeditions were sent to the Arctic and Antarctic circles, to Africa, to South and North America, and to the Pacific Ocean, while at numerous stations in India, Russia, Europe, and North and South America, hourly and simultaneous observations have been carried on for a long period, and in many places are still continued. In this way a great mass of facts has been accumulated, from a careful comparison of which the laws of terrestrial magnetism already announced have been educed or confirmed.

Perhaps the most remarkable result of these observations is the fact, first

47

established by them, that not only the greater variations in the earth's magnetism, but the most minute and irregular disturbances occur at the same instant in places the most distant from each other, showing a wonderful connection and coincidence in the causes of these phenomena throughout the world.

799. **Lines of magnetic force.**—The illustrious English philosopher, Faraday, has demonstrated that all matter is subject to magnetic influence.

As the evidence on which this important induction rests is chiefly derived from the use of electro-magnetism, its particular consideration is more conveniently referred to that subject. His general views, connected with terrestrial magnetism, may be thus stated. All space both above and within the limits of our atmosphere may be regarded as traversed *by lines of force,* among which are the lines of magnetic force. The condition of the space surrounding a magnet, or between its poles (777), may be taken as an illustration of this assumption. It is not more difficult to conceive of force existing without matter, than the converse, and it is certain that we know matter chiefly by the effects it produces on certain forces in nature. The lines of magnetic force are assumed to traverse void space without change, but when they come in contact with matter of any kind, they are either concentrated upon it, or dispersed, according to the nature of the matter. Thus we know that a suspended needle is attracted *axially* by a magnet, while a bar of bismuth, and many other solid, liquid, or gaseous bodies, similarly placed between the poles of a magnet, are held in a place at right angles to the axis, or *equatorially.* Hence all substances may be classified either as those which, like iron, point axially, and are called PARAMAGNETIC substances, and those which point equatorially, and termed DIAMAGNETIC. The force which urges bodies to the axial or equatorial lines is not a central force, but a force differing in character in the axial or radial directions. If a liquid paramagnetic body were introduced into the field of force, it would dilate axially, and form a prolate spheroid; while a liquid diamagnetic body would dilate equatorially, and form an oblate   546
spheroid.

The diagram, fig. 546, will serve to render more clear the action of diamagnetic and paramagnetic substances, upon the lines of magnetic force. Thus a diamagnetic substance, D, expands the lines of force, and causes them to open outwards, while a paramagnetic body, P, concentrates these lines upon itself. Bodies of the first class swing into the equator of force, or lie at right angles to the lines of force, while those of the paramagnetic class become axially arranged, parallel to the lines of force.

800. **Atmospheric magnetism.**—The discovery, by Faraday, of the highly paramagnetic character of oxygen gas, and of the neutral character of nitrogen, the two chief constituents of the atmosphere, is justly esteemed a fact of great importance in studying the phenomena of terrestrial magnetism. We thus see two-ninths of the atmosphere, by weight, consisting of a substance of eminent magnetic capacity, after the manner of iron, and liable to great physical changes of density, temperature, &c., and entirely independent of the solid earth. In this medium hang suspended the magnetic bars, which are used as

tests, and this magnetic medium is daily heated and cooled by the sun's rays, and its power of transmitting the lines of magnetic force is thus affected, influencing, undoubtedly, those diurnal changes already considered.

801. **Notions of the origin of the earth's magnetism.**—Two hypotheses have hitherto divided the opinions of philosophers in explaining the phenomena of terrestrial magnetism.

The older of these views (Hansteen's) assumes the existence of an independent magnetism in the earth, with its focus, or seat, near the earth's centre. This internal power manifests itself chiefly at four points near the surface, two of which, at the opposite ends of the supposed magnetic axis, are the most energetic, and are known as the magnetic poles. The minor poles have their own independent axis, and move around the principal axis from west to east in the western hemisphere, and the reverse in the southern, giving origin to the well-known phenomena of the secular variation of the needle. However well this hypothesis met the facts of terrestrial magnetism some years since, the rapid progress of our knowledge of magnetic phenomena, both terrestrial and general, within a short period, has materially changed scientific opinion. The diurnal and irregular variations in the magnetic forces, cannot be explained upon Hansteen's hypothesis, and especially the simultaneous occurrence of these disturbances at different points of observation. Nearly all bodies are now known to be susceptible to magnetic influence, while the maximum and minimum magnetic intensity are found in those regions of the globe where the minimum and maximum of superficial heat exist.

It is hence now argued, that the crust, or surface, and not the interior of the earth, is the seat of the magnetic force. That this force is manifested with least energy at the equator of magnetism, and with increasing power toward the poles, where, as in an artificial magnet, it attains its maximum development, because there we find the most perfect separation of the magnetic fluids : that the coercitive force (786) of the materials of the earth's surface is resolved by the solar heat, and that the depth to which this separation occurs is closely connected with the mean heat of the earth's crust, if not absolutely dependent upon it. Axes and poles have, therefore, in view of this hypothesis, no existence in fact, but are merely convenient mathematical terms for expressing our ideas of magnetic phenomena more closely, just as in crystallography we employ the same terms for the same reasons.

In conformity to this view, the manifestation of the magnetic forces will vary with all the diurnal changes of temperature, giving the relation of cause and effect between these changes, and the magnetic perturbations. The annual fluctuations in the mean temperature of the earth's surface will, therefore, be reproduced in corresponding movements in magnetic declination and dip. Hence, the magnetic meridian, and the system of isoclinal and isogonic curves ought to correspond closely, as they do with isothermal lines, and the peculiar distribution of temperature in both hemispheres. Indeed, we may assume, should this hypothesis prevail, that the differences now noticed between the isothermes and isogones (due, probably, to imperfect observations), will vanish under new and more extended researches.

IV. PRODUCTION OF MAGNETS.

802. **Artificial magnets** are produced (1.) by touch, or friction from

another magnet; (2.) by induction; (3.) by electrical currents; and (4.) by the solar rays.

The method by touch is accomplished by very various modes of manipulation, of which we shall describe only one or two, referring the reader to larger treatises on magnetism for fuller details. Since the introduction of the method by electro-magnetism, the old methods of producing magnets by touch are far less important than formerly.

The circumstances affecting the value of magnets, are chiefly the nature and hardness of the steel, the form and proportion of its parts, and the mode of keeping. The most uniform and fine-grained cast-steel, wrought with as little disturbance of its particles as possible, forms the best magnets.

547

This is tempered as high as possible, and the temper is then drawn by heat to a violet straw color, at which hardness it has been found to receive and retain a maximum of magnetism. The proportions of a bar magnet should be, for width, about one-twentieth the length; and the thickness, one-third to one-fourth the width. In a horse-shoe, the distance between the poles ought not to be greater than the width of one of the poles. The faces should be smooth and level, and the whole surface be highly polished. It is quite essential for preserving the power of a magnet, that its poles should be joined by a keeper or armature of soft iron, made to fit its level ends, and be suspended, as seen in fig. 547. Thus armed, a magnet gains power; but if left unarmed, it suffers material loss. Bar magnets are arranged as in fig. 548, either four magnets with their opposite poles in contact, or two magnetic bars, side by side, with two pieces of soft iron joining their opposite poles.

548

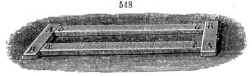

803. **Magnets by touch.**—Touch one pole of a powerful magnet with one end of a sewing-needle, or the point of a pen-knife, and it becomes instantly a magnet, attracting iron filings, and repelling or attracting the magnetic needle. The coercitive force has, in this case,

been decomposed by simple touch. If the magnet is very powerful, a near approach of the needle to it without contact will develop a feeble magnetism by induction.

More powerful magnetism is, however, developed by drawing the bar to be magnetized, from its centre to the end, several times over one pole of a magnet, returning it each time through the air, and repeating the stroke in the same direction. Then place the other pole in the middle of the bar, and stroke the opposite end as before.

Two magnets may be placed together, with their dissimilar poles in the middle of the bar, as in fig. 549, and then be moved in opposite directions, at a low

549

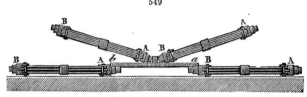

angle, to the extremities of the bar. The impregnation of the bar will be more powerful and speedy if it rests by its ends on the two opposite ends of two other magnets, as practiced by Coulomb. By inspecting the letters in fig. 549, this arrangement will be quite clear. Care is taken to prevent the ends of the two inclined bars from touching, by placing a bit of dry wood between them. This is called *single touch*, and is to be explained in accordance with ? 785.

To magnetize a bar by means of the *double touch*, two bars, or horse-shoe magnets are fastened together, with a wedge of dry wood between them, so that their dissimilar poles may be about a quarter of an inch asunder; or a horse-shoe magnet may be used if its poles are quite near together. The magnet, in this mode, is placed upright, on the middle of the bar, and is then rapidly drawn towards its end, taking care that neither of its poles glides over the end of the bar. The magnet is then passed over the opposite end of the bar as before. The poles will be dissimilar to those of the touching magnet.

550

804. **Horse-shoe magnets** are easily magnetized by connecting the open ends by a soft iron keeper, while another horse-shoe magnet of the same size is passed from the poles to the bend, in the direction of the arrow in fig. 550; the poles being arranged as indicated by the figure.

The easiest mode of obtaining a maximum magnetic effect in a bar, by touch, is that of Jacobi, viz.: to rest its ends against the poles of another magnet, and then to draw a piece of soft iron, called a feeder, from it several times along the bar. This mode is applied to horse-shoe magnets, as seen in fig. 551.

551

The dissimilar poles are placed together, and the feeder is drawn over the horse-shoe, in the direction of the arrow; when it reaches the curve, it is to be

47 *

replaced, and the process repeated ; turn the whole over without separating the poles, and treat the other side in like manner.

A horse-shoe of one pound weight may be thus charged, so that it will sustain 26·5 pounds. By the best method of touch before known, fig. 550, 21 lbs. 9 oz. was the highest attainable result. (Peschel.)

805. **Magnets by electro-magnetism.**—The mode of producing electro-magnetic currents will be hereafter described. By their means, powerful magnets of soft iron are easily produced, and, from these, by the methods of touch just described, very powerful artificial magnets may be made.

Logemann, of Haarlem, in Holland, has in this way produced the most powerful magnets ever made. One in possession of the author, sustained 28½ lbs. ; its own weight being 1 lb. The mode of producing these powerful magnets will be understood from fig. 552.

552

A spiral of insulated copper wire, t, is wound on a paste-board tube, A B, in the manner of the electro-magnetic helix. The bar to be magnetized is armed with two heavy cores, or cylinders of soft iron, S N, just fitting the inside of the spiral; when in its place,

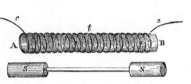

the ends of the spiral, $c\,z$, are connected with a few cells of Grove's or Bunsen's battery, and the powerful temporary magnetism induced in the masses of soft iron, reacts, to induce an uncommonly strong permanent magnetism in the bar of steel. A horse-shoe magnet is charged in a similar way, by encircling it with a helix of proper form, with similar armatures of soft iron. The close analogy of this mode to that of Jacobi, in the last section, will be noticed.

806. **Compound magnets** are made of several plates of steel, separately magnetized, as in fig. 523 and 549. As the coercitive power of steel appears to be overcome, chiefly, on its surfaces,

553

there is an advantage in multiplying the number of plates, but as each plate serves to neutralize a portion of the polarity of its neighbor (similar poles, of necessity, being brought into contact), there is soon found a limit beyond which there is no advantage in extending these batteries.

Large magnets are not as powerful, in proportion to their weight, as small ones. Sir Isaac Newton is said to have worn in his finger-ring a magnet (lodestone) weighing three grains, and capable of sustaining over 250 times its own weight (760 grains). A lodestone of three or four pounds weight, mounted as in fig. 534, can rarely sustain over two or three times its own weight.

The most powerful artificial magnet on record, was that made by Dr. G. Knight, of London, and now in possession of the Royal Society. It consisted of two prismatic bundles, **each** of 240 powerful bar magnets five feet in length, mounted on wheels; between the end plates of this combination, the poles of the most energetic single magnet were reversed or powerfully reinforced.

807. **Magnetism of steel by the sun's rays.**—Although the fact is doubted by some experimenters, the weight of testimony appears to support the conclusion, that the sun's violet rays possess the power of inducing permanent magnetism, when concentrated by a lens, on steel needles.

808. **To deprive a magnet of its power,** it is only necessary to reverse the order adopted to impart magnetism to it, stroking it from the ends to the centre with poles of the same name opposed. In this way the magnetic virtue may be wholly or very nearly destroyed.

The approach of a feeble magnet to a strong one may reverse its polarity. Leaving a magnet without its keeper greatly impairs its power. Suddenly jerking it off the keeper, or striking it with a hammer, in a way to make it vibrate, does the same. Heat accomplishes the total destruction of magnetism, and in short, anything which weakens its coercitive power. Conversely, hanging an armed magnet in the position it would assume if free to obey the solicitation of the forces of terrestrial magnetism, is the best position to favor its greatest development. Every magnet which has been charged while its poles are connected by a keeper, possesses more power before the keeper is removed than after. It is indeed overcharged, and the excess may be likened to that residual force which retains the keeper of an electro-magnet in its place after the circuit which excited it is broken, or to the residual charge of a Leyden jar. Every time the keeper of a magnet is moved suddenly, a loss of power is sustained, and hence the keeper should be removed by sliding it gradually off endways, and only when it is required for the performance of an experiment.

PERMANENT MAGNETS

A Book by
JOHN WALTER ESTERLINE
President of The Esterline Company

Published by
THE ESTERLINE COMPANY
INDIANAPOLIS

Introduction —

IN the year 1896, Mr. J. W. Esterline, the author of this booklet, became interested in the subject of magnetism, and began an experimental study which extended over a period of ten years, he having been during this time with the department of Electrical Engineering of Purdue University at Lafayette, Indiana.

This research work embraced a study of the qualities of iron and steel used in the manufacture of electrical machinery and apparatus of all classes, the practical determination of these qualities and their application to the design of the magnetic circuits of electrical apparatus. This work resulted also in the development of a number of types of apparatus for testing magnetic materials and permanent magnets, many of which are used by electrical manufacturers and steel mills.

Mr. Esterline was for a number of years the chairman of the Committee on Magnetic Testing of the American Society for Testing Materials, which was appointed for the purpose of standardizing methods of testing and specifications for magnetic materials. In the past years a considerable portion of his available time has been given to expert work on this subject in connection with the production and use of iron and steel for magnetic circuits.

The Esterline Company began the manufacture of permanent magnets for the trade eighteen years ago and this product of the company has been and is today made under his personal direction. This fact, together with the accumulated experience of years in the perfecting of processes and the development of an organization and a skilled personnel, are the basis for the generally accepted fact that a permanent magnet bearing the trade mark NE is representative of the best that can be made.

THE ESTERLINE COMPANY,

January, 1919.   Indianapolis, Indiana.

Permanent Magnets

ALTHOUGH a vast amount of scientific investigation has been done, and a great deal has been written on the subject of permanent magnets, it remains one upon which very little practical, useful information exists. The reason for this is the fact that no laws have yet been discovered, fixing any relation between the qualities of a permanent magnet, and the character of the materials and the conditions of manufacture, upon which the magnetic qualities of the magnet depend.

Any one who has the means for forming, hardening and magnetizing a piece of steel, can make a permanent magnet of some sort, but to manufacture permanent magnets of uniformly high magnetic quality, requires something of the scientist, the chemist and the metallurgist, together with the requisite special equipment and an organization experienced in this class of work.

THE IMPORTANCE OF QUALITY.

In the majority of cases, the purpose for which permanent magnets are used is such that the quality, accuracy, efficiency or usefulness of the machines or instruments of which they form a part, depend directly upon the magnetic qualities of the permanent magnets used. In electrical measuring and recording instruments the maintenance of accuracy depends absolutely upon the retentivity of the magnets. In the case of magnetos, efficiency and successful operation are both determined by the quality of the magnets.

The qualities of a permanent magnet, that is, the characteristics which determine its quality as a magnet, remain unchanged indefinitely. They are a characteristic of the particular piece of steel, in its particular state, just as its hardness, tensile strength or elastic limit. A great many persons confuse state of magnetization with magnetic quality, whereas they mean totally different things. Demagnetizing a magnet changes its state of magnetization, but does not alter its quality; a finished piece has, before it is magnetized, the qualities which determine how good a magnet it will be when magnetized. The quality of a magnet can be affected only by some treatment which will at the same time affect its physical characteristics, such as by heating or annealing.

THE IMPORTANCE OF UNIFORMITY.

The design of a machine or instrument in which permanent magnets are used, is, of course, based upon some known or assumed qualities of the magnets to be used, and good design requires that the magnet, in its design, be adapted to the use to be made of it, and the conditions under which it is to operate. When this has been done,

Page Four

it is necessary that the magnets be uniform in quality, otherwise the finished product will vary in quality, accuracy or efficiency by the same amounts the magnets do.

This uniformity of magnetic quality is especially important where two or more magnets are acting in parallel on the same magnetic circuit, because so placing magnets of unequal strength and retentivity has an effect similar to that obtained by placing batteries or generators of different voltage in parallel. The same statement holds true for magnets made up of two or more leaves, and in the design and manufacture of compound magnets, it is a matter of importance to see that the several portions are so related and of such uniformity that they will operate properly together.

For the same reason it follows that maximum magnetic quality in a magnet of considerable cross-section, can only be obtained by the use of steel of an analysis, and a treatment, which will insure uniform quality throughout the cross-section of the magnet. It is this feature which limits the cross-section which can be successfully used, and makes necessary the use of steel of different chemical content, subjected to correspondingly different treatment, if the best results are to be obtained in magnets of different cross-section.

The Esterline Permameter for the Rapid and Accurate Testing of Magnet Steel and Permanent Magnets

THE QUALITIES OF PERMANENT MAGNETS.

Generally speaking, there are two things which are a measure of the quality of a permanent magnet. These are usually called the magnetic qualities. They are:

(1) The residual induction or residual magnetic flux.

(2) The retentivity or coercive force.

While these two qualities or characteristics are somewhat related, in so far as the conditions which affect them are concerned, the existence of maximum residual induction does not necessarily imply that the retentivity is a maximum, or vice versa. The best permanent magnet is the one in which both these qualities are at the maximum value obtainable, and it requires long experience in the selection of steel and the utmost care and skill in the treatment of it to produce permanent magnets which are uniformly high in both residual induction and retentivity.

Almost all kinds of steel which can be tempered will retain a portion of their initial magnetism if magnetized. There are, however, very few kinds of steel which make relatively good permanent magnets, and the quality of the magnets made from any kind of steel depends upon a great many different things, viz.:

(1) Chemical content.
(2) Conditions under which the billets are made.
(3) Rolling conditions.
(4) Annealing.
(5) Furnace conditions and treatment during the forming or forging of the magnets.
(6) Conditions under which the final heat treatment is done.
(7) The mechanical operations performed after final heat treatment.
(8) The process of maturing.
(9) Method of magnetizing.

It is clear, therefore, that from the time the steel is melted until the magnet is finished there are conditions and processes which materially affect its final quality as a magnet, and the matter is still further complicated by the fact that the effect of one condition or process on the quality of the magnet may depend upon one or more of the other variable conditions.

For example, the result obtained from different heat treatments

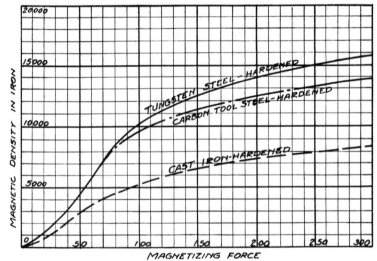

Fig. 1.—*Induction curves of three specimens of hardened metals. The values along the horizontal line show intensity of the magnetic field in air and the values along the vertical line, corresponding intensity in the metal when placed in the air field.*

Page Six

may depend somewhat upon the chemical analysis. The fact that a change in one may alter the effect of a change in another condition, necessitates the keeping of continuous records of all the conditions, in order to so control them as to produce a product of maximum quality and uniformity.

In Fig. "1" are the magnetization curves of three kinds of iron; these curves show the relation between the magnetizing force, or the magnetic field in the air surrounding the iron, and the corresponding magnetic density in the iron itself when acted upon by the field in the air. These curves show the relative ease with which these materials are magnetized, but have nothing to do with their ability to retain magnetism.

They are important nevertheless, because a permanent magnet is required to drive its magnetic flux throughout its own length, as well as through the magnetic circuit upon which it is operating. It follows therefore that any condition in manufacture which increases the magnetic resistance or reluctance of a magnet without a corresponding increase in the retentivity is detrimental to its quality.

In Fig. "2" are shown the hysteresis curves of the same three pieces of iron. These curves are obtained by magnetizing the iron to a known maximum magnetic density, represented by the point "A" on the curve. The magnetizing force is then gradually reduced, the magnetic density falling along the curve as indicated by the arrow.

At the point "B," where the curve crosses the line of zero magnetizing force, the distance O-B represents the strength of the residual or permanent magnetism. If, now, the magnetizing force be reversed in direction and applied so as to reduce the residual magnetism, the

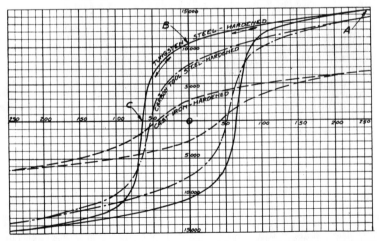

Fig. 2.—*Hysteresis Curves of Hardened Metals. The point A represents the maximum induction, B the residual induction, and C the retentivity, for the hardened tungsten steel specimen.*

magnetic density will continue to decrease until it becomes zero, where the curve crosses the horizontal axis at "C."

The demagnetizing force represented by the value O-C is that force necessary to balance the magnetizing force of the magnet itself; it is a measure of the difficulty of demagnetizing the magnet, or of the power with which the magnet holds its magnetism. This quality is known as the retentivity or coercive force. The vertical distance O-B is therefore the measure of the residual magnetism, or residual induction, and denotes the strength of the magnet in so far as its magnetic flux is concerned, whereas the distance O-C represents the retentivity or the tenacity with which the magnet holds its magnetism.

Both of these qualities are of extreme importance, and it cannot be said that one is more important than the other. High magnetic strength is of little value if that strength is not made stable by a high retentivity. Neither can a magnet be said to be of high quality if its retentivity be high and its strength low. Referring to Fig. "2," it will be noted that the retentivity of hardened cast iron is approximately 75 per cent. that of hardened tungsten steel, while the residual density of cast iron is only about 30 per cent. of that of a tungsten magnet.

It should be borne in mind, however, that both the magnetic strength and retentivity of any finished magnet depend upon the varying conditions of manufacture which we have named above. Even with material of the same analysis it is possible to make magnets of the same magnetic strength, but varying widely in retentivity; and it is also possible by varying the conditions to make from the same steel magnets of the same retentivity, but varying widely in residual magnetism. In fact, it is quite difficult, using the same material, to keep from making magnets which vary in one or the other quality.

In Fig. "2" the curves shown are the result of carrying the magnetization and demagnetization through a complete cycle, but one-fourth of this cycle is all that is required in order to determine the qualities of a magnet, as shown in Fig "3." Attention is called to the fact that in the foregoing curves the magnetic density is expressed in the flux or magnetic lines per unit area, and the coercive or retentivity is given per unit of length; it follows, therefore, that the total magnetic strength of a magnet having given residual flux per unit area is proportional to its cross-sectional area, and the ability of a magnet of given retentivity to hold its magnetism is proportional to its length; that is, the length of the bar from which it is made.

THE EFFECT OF AN AIR GAP BETWEEN POLES.

In making tests such as are indicated in the results plotted in Fig. "2" and Fig. "3," the magnet under test constitutes the entire magnetic circuit. The curves give the result which would be obtained if the magnet were a closed ring with no air gap between the poles. In other words, they represent the quality of the steel as a magnet, and that alone. The useful flux of a permanent magnet operating across an air-gap is always less than the flux which the magnet would give with no gap between its poles, or when magnetically "short-circuited." On account of the very high reluctance or magnetic resistance of air the residual magnetism of a magnet of a given length is lessened as the air path between the poles is increased, and right here comes a very important consideration in the design of apparatus embodying the use of permanent magnets.

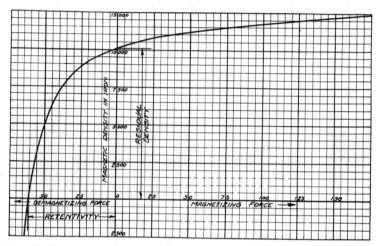

Fig. 3.—Portion of Hysteresis Loop Necessary to Show the Qualities of a Permanent Magnet.

Referring to Fig. "3," it will be noted that as the demagnetizing force is increased from O, the residual magnetism reduces very slowly at first, and that as the demagnetizing force is increased the magnetism falls more and more rapidly, until finally it comes down along an almost vertical line. This indicates that for moderate demagnetizing forces the permanent magnetism is fairly stable, but that if the demagnetizing action be carried beyond a certain value the flux becomes unstable and the magnet will not recover its strength when the demagnetizing force is removed.

Since the introduction of an air gap between the poles of a permanent magnet has the effect of partially demagnetizing it, and the extent of demagnetization depends upon the relative length of the magnet and the air gap, it is important that the ratio of length of magnet to length of air gap be such that the magnet will not be demagnetized by the air gap to the point where magnetization becomes unstable. In some types of apparatus the permanent magnets used are required to operate in opposition to a coil of wire carrying an electric current, as in the case of a magneto, the demagnetizing effect of which is added to that caused by the air gap, and in designing apparatus of this character it is important to take into account the effects of both the air gap and the coil.

If the magnetization in a permanent magnet be once reduced to

Page Nine

the point where it becomes unstable, the magnet will not recover, so that it is important to bear in mind that the characteristics of the magnet and the magnetic circuit on which it operates must be such that the maximum reduction of flux under any condition of operation must not be to a point where the flux becomes unstable.

Since the retentivity of a magnet is the measure of its stability in opposition to demagnetizing effects, the reader will readily see that this quality is of equal, if not greater importance, than the magnetic strength. It is possible, by the proper selection of steel and the use of a heat treatment corresponding to the characteristics of the steel, to produce magnets of uniformly high retentivity without sacrificing magnetic strength. It is also possible by using a heat treatment adapted to the character of the steel to obtain maximum strength without a sacrifice in retentivity.

In the design of apparatus in which permanent magnets are to be used, it is important that the total cross section of the permanent magnets used shall be such as to give the requisite flux under actual operating conditions and that the length of the magnets, i. e. the effective length of the magnet from pole to pole, shall be such as to enable it to withstand all the demagnetizing effects to which it is subjected without suffering a serious reduction in its intensity. Other things being unchanged, the total flux of a permanent magnet is proportional to its cross-section, and the ability of a magnet to withstand demagnetizing forces is proportional to its length.

It is essential, for the best results, that the magnet be selected or designed for the magnetic circuit on which it is to operate, and for any magnetic circuit considered there is a cross-section and length of permanent magnet which will give the maximum flux, with the requisite stability, using a minimum amount of magnet steel.

Product of Strength and Retentivity a Measure of Quality

The author has long maintained that for the majority of uses to which permanent magnets are applied, the product (strength x retentivity) is the best measure of magnetic quality. This has been demonstrated many times in tests which have been conducted when designing permanent magnets for our customers. An example is given in Fig. "4." After having decided all the questions relating to the analysis of the steel, the length and cross-section of the magnets to be used on this particular machine, which was a high tension magneto, the next step was to determine that treatment of the steel which would give the customer the best results.

One hundred magnets were made of the selected quality of steel; these were divided into ten sets of ten magnets each, and each set was quenched under varying conditions. A magneto, operated at constant speed, was fitted with these magnets and the output across an air gap of one-tenth inch and the current on short circuit were measured. The average of the results from each set of magnets is plotted in Fig. "4."

In this figure are plotted the residual strength and retentivity of

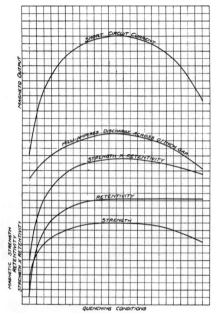

Fig. 4.—Curves Determined by Actual Tests Showing the Relation Between the Qualities of Permanent Magnets and the Output of Magnetos Using These Magnets. The Variation in Quality was Obtained by Varying the Quenching Conditions, Using the Same Chemical Analysis. These Curves Show Clearly the Importance of Magnets of the Proper Quality.

the magnets as obtained with different quenching conditions, and from this is plotted a curve of strength x retentivity. Corresponding with these curves are plotted the output curves of the magneto, using the magnets quenched under the different conditions, and it will be noted that maximum output was obtained using those magnets, the product of whose strength and retentivity was the highest.

We are not free to conclude, however, that the same methods of manufacture would apply for steel of a different analysis, or even for magnets of a different cross-section, as both the chemical content and the cross-section must be considered in fixing the heat treatment. The curves do show, however, that the quality of the magnets is expressed by the product strength x retentivity and that the efficiency and stability of the customer's apparatus is dependent upon the quality and uniformity of the magnets which he uses.

AGING OR MATURING OF MAGNETS.

In some classes of apparatus, particularly electrical indicating, integrating and recording instruments, the maintenance of the initial calibration and accuracy of the instruments requires that the magnets be brought to as stable a magnetic condition as possible before the in-

Page Eleven

strument is calibrated. This is called aging or maturing of the magnets. Bringing a magnet into a condition where its flux will be stable requires two things, viz.:

(1) A physical treatment of the steel after quenching, which makes further changes in its structure, molecular condition or magnetic quality improbable.

(2) A magnetic treatment of the magnet after magnetization, which will make changes in its state of magnetization, under the conditions of ordinary operation, improbable.

When a magnet is hardened it, of course, undergoes very rapid structural changes, and for a time after quenching there is a change in condition taking place, quite rapidly at first and gradually decreasing until the physical properties become stable. This stability of structural state of the steel can be hastened by physical treatment, which process is called aging, or maturing. Obviously the treatment applied must be such as to only age the steel without impairing its magnetic qualities.

As has been already stated, it is possible after magnetizing a magnet to bring it to a state of magnetization, in which the total or useful flux will not be greatly altered by such demagnetizing action as that to which the magnet will be subjected in use, provided, of course, it is properly designed for the magnetic circuit on which it is used. It should be clearly understood that this treatment does not alter the retentivity of the magnet, but simply changes the magnetic state in such a manner that the ratio of change in flux to magnetizing or demagnetizing effects is reduced at that part of the magnetic cycle represented by the state of residual magnetization.

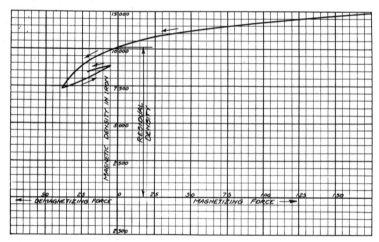

Fig. 5.—Showing the Magnetic Cycle Through Which a Permanent Magnet is Put in Order to Render the Flux More Stable.

Page Twelve

In Fig "3" we have given a curve showing the relation between residual density and magnetizing and demagnetizing forces, from the point of maximum magnetization to complete demagnetization, when the change from the one state to the other is gradual and uninterrupted. It will be noted that upon the application of a demagnetizing force, the residual induction begins to drop and as the force is increased the reduction becomes more rapid, until a point is reached where the curve is almost parallel to the flux ordinate.

This means that with a magnet in this state of magnetization the flux of the magnet will vary along this curve when the magnet is subjected to any exterior magnetizing or demagnetizing force, such as the action of a coil, stray fields, etc. In order to make the value of the residual flux as stable as possible, it is necessary to have the curve as nearly parallel as possible to the horizontal axis.

In Fig. "5" is shown the curve of a magnet taken as it is put through this stabilizing process. The arrows indicate the direction of magnetization or demagnetization. After the magnet has been fully magnetized, a demagnetizing force is applied, which removes a portion of the flux. It is next subjected to a magnetizing force, and then to a demagnetizing effect, which has the effect of bringing the curve more nearly parallel to the base line, although the residual induction is somewhat reduced. It is obvious that this treatment should be applied after the magnetic circuit on which the magnet is to operate has been completely assembled.

MATERIALS OF MANUFACTURE.

Permanent magnets can be made of cast iron, from steel carrying anywhere from .3 to 1.5 per cent. of carbon, or from alloy steel containing carbon, together with tungsten, molybdemum, chromium or vanadium. Cast iron magnets are used principally in galvanometers and similar apparatus, where wieght is not objectionable and efficiency is not a matter of importance.

CARBON STEEL MAGNETS.

For some classes of work, where space and weight are not of importance, magnets made of a good grade of open hearth carbon steel are used. By a careful selection of such steel with reference to its carbon, manganese, sulphur and phosphorus content, it is possible by proper heat treatment to produce magnets having a flux of magnetic strength of about 75 per cent. that of tungsten or chromium steel magnets of the same cross-section and a retentivity of about 70 per cent. of that of the better grades of steels just named.

TUNGSTEN STEEL.

For many years prior to the outbreak of the European war the alloy steel most commonly, in fact almost universally used in the manufacture of high-grade permanent magnets, was one containing principally carbon, tungsten and chromium, and in which the percentage of manganese, sulphur and phosphorus were kept near the lowest practical limits. Such an alloy, if properly made in the steel mill and intelligently processed in the magnet-making plant, will produce magnets of high strength and permanence.

During the first year of the war, due both to the very high cost and the inability to obtain the metal tungsten in sufficient quantities to meet the demand for the production of high-speed alloy steel, which contains from 12 to 20 per cent. tungsten, it was necessary to develop other alloys for use in the manufacture of permanent magnets, in which development work the author was able to take some part.

From the beginning it was clear to those having had experience with the various alloys, that to successfully replace tungsten steel in the manufacture of permanent magnets would require a development in the methods of manufacture and heat treatment as well as the determination of an alloy which would give the results, the greatest advantage of tungsten steel being the comparatively low percentage of carbon, permitting of ease in drilling and machining, and the simplicity of the heat treatment required.

CHROMIUM STEEL.

The author's experience has entirely borne out this opinion, since by the use of chromium alloys produced under correct conditions and treated according to processes particularly adapted to them, magnets are being produced which, from the standpoint of both strength and retentivity, are the equal of the tungsten product. It is a fact, however, that the chromium alloys do not permit of as wide a range in manufacturing and heat treating conditions as tungsten steel, but with

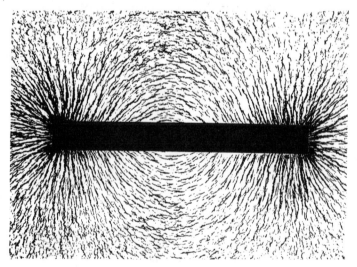

Fig. 6.—A Bar Magnet and the Paths Taken by the Magnetic Lines in Their Passage Through the Air from One Pole to the Other.

Page Fourteen

the proper and uniform conditions the product shows greater uniformity than was the case with the tungsten alloy. In other words, the average results with chromium alloy steel are in every way equal to those obtained with tungsten steel, and the product does not vary from the average by nearly so wide a margin as in the case of the tungsten alloy.

TYPES OF MAGNETS.

The type and design of a permanent magnet depends largely upon the purpose for which it is to be used. The simplest form is the bar magnet, used principally for experimental and instructional purposes, for maintaining controlling fields, and in compasses and similar instruments. In Fig. "6" is shown a bar magnet and the paths of its field of flux. On account of the fact that its poles are far apart, a bar magnet is the weakest form of permanent magnet.

Horseshoe magnets are made in a variety of sizes and are used for a great many purposes. Toy magnets are usually of this type, and large sizes of horseshoe magnets are used for the purpose of removing particles of iron from various materials. In Fig. "7" is illustrated a typical magnet of the horseshoe type; the length of the bar used is long in comparison with the distance between the poles, and the short distance between the poles with a gradual widening of the space between the sides of the magnet, render it a very efficient form.

In Fig "8" is shown a type of mill magnet which has in the past been largely used for separating metals from other materials; this photograph is taken from a sample submitted by one of our prospective customers. A magnet of this shape is less efficient than that shown in Fig. "7," due to the excessive leakage between the adjacent

Fig. 7.—*Horse-shoe Magnet, Made in a Variety of Sizes, for Use as Toys and in Larger Sizes for Separating Particles of Iron from Grain, Clay Slop, Cut Tobacco, Etc.*

Page Fifteen

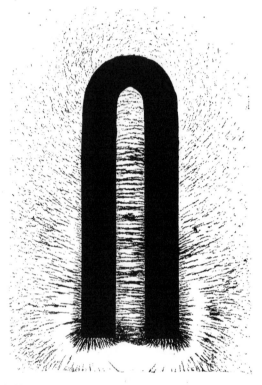

Fig. 8.—Magnetic Field of a U-Shaped Mill Magnet. Note the Leakage of Flux Between the Poles Due to the Improper Shape of the Magnet.

pole faces. In Fig. "9" is shown a photograph of the field of the horseshoe magnet illustrated in Fig. "7," and the concentration of the flux at the poles is clearly shown in this figure. The type of magnet shown in Figs. "7" and "9" is found very efficient for mill work, and is likewise very permanent in the maintenance of its flux.

In Fig. "10" is illustrated the standard form of single leaf U-shaped magnet commonly used on electrical instruments and high-grade magnetos. These magnets are drilled and countersunk to accommodate screws for holding them in place. After quenching and be-

Fig. 9.—*Flux Field of a Horseshoe Mill Magnet. Note the Strong Concentration of the Field at the Poles.*

Fig. 10.—*Typical U-Shaped Magneto Magnet. The Magnet is Drilled and Countersunk for Screws Which Hold it in Place, and the Inner Side of the Poles are Ground to a Smooth Surface.*

Page Seventeen

fore being magnetized the inner surface of the poles are ground to a smooth surface to fit the poles to which the magnets are attached. Magnets of this type are made in various widths and thicknesses.

The author's experience has been to the effect that the width of a U-shaped magnet can be increased to a much greater degree than the thickness without seriously affecting the quality of the magnet. There are two reasons why this is true. If both the width and the thickness be increased the mass of the metal to be hardened increases more rapidly than the area exposed to the cooling medium, and the magnet is likely to be soft in the center, which condition detracts from the magnetic strength. When one dimension is kept within reasonably small limits, and the other dimension is increased, the cooling area increases proportionately and it is possible to make magnets of steel 3 inches or 3½ inches in width if the thickness does not exceed ⅜ inch or 7/16 inch.

As the thickness of a magnet is increased, the difference between the inside and the outside length becomes greater, the effect of which

Fig. 11.—This is an illustration of a double-width magnet which replaced two of the single magnets shown in the right of the figure. It is frequently possible to make a saving by using wide magnets of this type. With steel of the proper analysis and a corresponding heat treatment this can be done without sacrificing magnetic strength or retentivity.

is the same as that of putting in parallel two magnets of different length, and this fact limits the thickness of the steel which can be used if the best results are to be obtained.

On account of the fact that the increased width of a magnet, if the thickness is not too great, does not increase the difficulty of hardening, it has been found possible in many cases to make a single magnet of double width replace two single magnets. In Fig. "11" is illustrated such a magnet, made of steel 2x⅜ inch, which replaced two magnets each 1x⅜ inch, with equally good results. The cost of a single magnet of double width is obviously less than that of two narrower magnets, for the reason that the number of operations and the number of handlings in manufacture is reduced one-half.

In Fig. "12" is illustrated a typical double leaf magnet, largely used on ignition magnetos. Where the thickness of steel required is such that it cannot be hardened in a single piece, double leaf magnets are resorted to, the outer leaf being a close fit over the inner. Contrary to what might be expected, placing an outer leaf of the same cross-section over the inner leaf of a magnet will not double the flux. This is due to the fact that the effective length of the outer is greater than the effective length of that portion of the inner leaf with which it is acting in parallel, so that the outer leaf tends to weaken or sub-

Fig. 12.—*Typical Double-Leaf Magnet, Used Where the Cross Section Would be Too Great to Harden in One Piece. In Double-Leaf Magnets the Relative Length of the Inner and Outer Leaves Must be Kept Within Proper Limits.*

tract some of the flux from the inner. This effect is more pronounced as the thickness of the leaves increase in proportion to their length; as the length of the bars of which the leaves are made is increased, the difference between the effective length of the outer and inner leaves will be a less percentage of the effective length.

In magnets made of $\frac{1}{2}$x$1\frac{1}{2}$ inch steel, with an opening between the poles of 2 inches, and the magnets 6 inches high overall, the writer has found that the addition of the outer leaf did not increase the strength of the magnet, but actually decreased it, so that the inner leaf alone gave more flux than the entire magnet when the outer leaf was added. Some years ago, in the design of a permanent magnet to be capable of lifting a weight of 100 pounds, the author found that in making a U-shaped magnet of eight leaves of steel, each $\frac{3}{8}$x2 inches, the addition of the three outer leaves actually weakened the magnet. This difficulty was overcome by making two straight legs of magnet steel composed of eight leaves each $\frac{3}{8}$x2 inches, all the pieces being the same length, and bolted between these two legs was a soft iron yoke; this construction produced a magnet of the required strength.

In Fig. "13" is shown a triple leaf magnet made of quite thin steel, and the characteristics of this magnet were such that it was necessary to magnetize the magnets after they were in place on the magneto in order to prevent the outer leaves from reducing the flux, and also on account of the fact that the length of the magnet is short in comparison with the distance between the poles.

Fig. 13.—*Triple Leaf Magnet. The Distance Between the Poles and the Cross Section of This Magnet Are Rather Great for the Length.*

In the manufacture of electrical instruments, magnets are sometimes used made of either bars bent on edge or of a number of pieces stamped from a sheet and assembled together, the pole pieces being formed in the ends of the magnet. In Fig. "14" is shown a circular magnet of this type, and in Fig. "15" is a photograph of the field flux of such a magnet. Such magnets are quite expensive to produce, if required to be accurate, on account of the necessity of grinding the polar space after the magnet has been quenched, but perhaps the saving of the usual soft iron pole pieces may offset this higher cost.

In Fig. "16" are shown three types of magnets used in less expensive ammeters and voltmeters. In the middle figure is a magnet the poles of which are formed from the bar itself, thus obviating the use

Fig. 14.—*Circular Magnet Used in Electrical Instruments, in Which the Pole Pieces are Formed by the Magnet Poles. Such Magnets are Expensive, but Reduce the Number of Parts in Instruments.*

of soft iron pole pieces. These illustrations are two-thirds full size. In the manufacture of alternating and direct current watthour meters, permanent magnets are used for brakes to the rotating element, and

Page Twenty

Fig. 15.—*Photograph of the Field of Flux of a Circular Instrument Magnet. Note the Intense Field at and Near the Poles.*

in Figs. "17" and "18" are illustrated some typical watthour meter magnets, of which a large variety of types and designs are used in this country and abroad. Since the sustained accuracy of the watthour meter depends upon the constancy of the strength of the magnet, it is important that they be of high permanence, and they should, of course, be carefully matured and properly magnetized, if the best results are to be obtained.

States of Magnetization.

When magnets have been properly manufactured, heat treated and matured, there are other precautions which must be observed in

Fig. 16.—*Magnets for Small Direct Current Voltmeters and Ammeters.*

Page Twenty-one

Fig. 17.—*Typical Watthour Meter Brake Magnets.*

the subsequent handling and application of the magnets, if the best results from them are to be obtained. When a number of magnets are shipped in one box in a magnetized condition, even though they be fitted with keepers or nested in pairs, the magnetic fields set up are

Fig. 18.—*Typical Watthour Meter Brake Magnets.*

sure to somewhat affect the magnetic state of the magnets, and each magnet should be properly magnetized at the proper stage in the manufacture of the instrument or the apparatus on which it is to be used. After magnets have been finally magnetized they should never be piled

Fig. 19.—*Field of a Properly Magnetized Magnet.*

Page Twenty-two

or laid on each other, otherwise local magnetic fields will be set up which detract from the strength of the magnet itself.

The process of magnetizing, whether done before or after the apparatus is assembled, should be such as to fully saturate the magnet uniformly throughout its entire length, and the author's experience has been to the effect that not every means of magnetizing accomplishes this result. In Fig. "19" is shown a photograph of the magnetic field of a large U-shaped magnet properly magnetized. It will be noted that the field shows a concentration of the flux at the poles, and

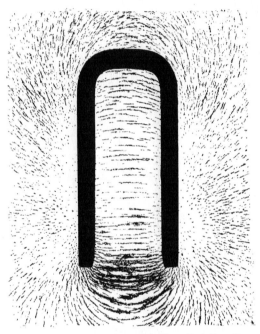

Fig. 20.—Field on an Improperly Magnetized Magnet.

that with the exception of the leakage from pole to pole, the field about the magnet is almost neutral except at the poles. In Fig. "20" is shown the field of the same magnet magnetized by a method very commonly used; namely, that of placing magnets on the poles of a large electro-magnet. It will be noted that the field about the body of this magnet is far from neutral, and a large portion of the flux circulates about the magnet in paths which are not useful. The tests of this

Page Twenty-three

magnet when magnetized by the two methods gave the following results:

Properly magnetized—strength 56, retentivity 92.

Improperly magnetized—strength 47, retentivity 90.

In Fig. "21" is shown a photograph of the field of a U-shaped magnet properly magnetized, and in Fig "22" is a field of the same magnet when magnetized by the method of influence from an electromagnet. The stray field set up about the magnet and the increased

Fig. 21.—Field of a Magnet Properly Saturated.

leakage are clearly shown in Fig. "22." In the case of double leaf magnets, the magnet should be magnetized after the two leaves have been assembled. In Fig. "23" is shown a photograph of the field of flux about a double leaf magnet properly magnetized, while in Fig. "24" is shown the field about the same magnet when the two leaves were magnetized separately and then shoved together. Not only did the outer leaf partially demagnetize the inner in the process of assembling, but set up intermediate poles clearly shown by the photograph of the flux field.

Page Twenty-four

Frequently in assembling machines the magnets are considerably weakened by bringing them into contact with each other in such a manner that the entire effective length of one magnet is opposed to and demagnetizes the shorter portion of the neighboring magnet. In Fig. "25," when the second magnet is applied without a keeper, in passing down alongside the first magnet it will partially demagnetize the latter. Using a keeper as shown in Fig. "26" will partially ob-

Fig. 22.—*Field of a Magnet Charged by Means of an Electro-Magnet.*

viate this difficulty, but the keeper should never be slid off the magnet from its poles toward the yoke, otherwise it will partially demagnetize the magnet. The keeper should be pulled straight away from the poles of the magnet when it is removed, and it should be of soft iron of a cross-section equal to at least 50 per cent. of that of the magnet itself.

It is impossible to lay down a definite rule or recommendation for the magnetizing and application of the magnets to machines of various kinds, but it is safe to say that there is one right way to do it in each case, and a number of wrong ways, and a little experience accompanied by tests will usually indicate the proper procedure.

COST OF MAGNETS.

The factors which determine or affect the cost of a magnet are the weight of the steel required; the labor cost and the percentage of rejections. The only way to reduce the weight of a magnet for a given purpose is to properly design it for the purpose for which it is to be used, and when this has been done, this element of the cost is fixed.

Fig. 23.—Field of a Double-Leaf or Compound Magnet Magnetized as a Unit.

The labor cost is determined by the simplicity or complexity of the magnet in form or shape, the number and character of the operations necessary to produce it, the accuracy to which it is required to adhere, and the number manufactured in a given period. Many magnets as originally designed are needlessly complicated in shape, and we have very frequently co-operated with our customers in simplifying designs and thereby reducing the cost of manufacture, as well as the cost and maintenance of tools. Magnet steel, if of a chemical content necessary to give the best results magnetically, is difficult to machine even in an annealed state, and this means that a single machine oper-

Page Twenty-six

ation, such as drilling or countersinking, also entails an annealing operation if steel of the proper analysis for the best results is used. Milling machine operations and the tapping of threads in magnet steel are especially difficult and should be avoided if at all possible.

Practically all magnets are forged and worked hot, which involves the problem of shrinkage and excessive wear of tools; there is likewise some shrinkage and warping in hardening, so that the more accurately a magnet must be held to fixed tolerances, the greater will be the cost of making and the percentage of rejections.

The number of magnets to be made within a given period affects the cost in two ways: First, there is the greater economy which can

Fig. 24.—Field of a Compound Magnet in Which the Two Leaves Were Magnetized Separately.

be obtained in making a larger number at one "set up" of the equipment, and secondly, the character of the tool equipment for producing a given magnet, is determined largely by the number of magnets of that particular kind the manufacturer knows he will be called upon to produce, and the character of this equipment in turn affects the cost of production.

Page Twenty-seven

SPECIFICATIONS FOR QUALITY.

Specifications for strength and retentivity should be such as to allow for the variation which is sure to be obtained in a commercial product, and should fix the average values and how much variation from the average will be permissible. When it is possible to submit samples to the manufacturer showing the character of the workmanship desired, this will enable the manufacturer to determine with accuracy the percentage of rejection which may be expected. Where

Fig. 25.—Incorrect Method of Applying Magnets. The Second Magnet, When Applied Without a Keeper, Partially Demagnetizes the First Magnet.

such samples are not available it has been found desirable to fix the specifications after a quantity of the magnets have been manufactured, since it is almost impossible to make up a few sample magnets which will be representative of the regular run of manufacture.

The quantity of magnets covered by a given order or contract determines to a great extent the character of the tools which the manufacturer is justified in making up for their production, which in turn affect the cost, so that it is always desirable from the standpoint of the purchaser to contract in as large quantities as are justifiable, even though the shipments may be distributed over a considerable period. We have always made it our policy to co-operate with our customers

Fig. 26.—Correct Method of Applying Magnets. The Keeper, However, Should Not be Slid Upward on the Magnet, but Pulled Straight Away from It, Before the Magnet is Pushed Into Position.

in the design of magnets, as well as in the determination of those points which fix the standards of production.

STANDARD MAGNETS.

As a rule permanent magnets are not carried in stock, but are made on order in accordance with customer's drawings. In many cases, where a limited number are required, it is advisable for the purchaser to get in touch with us before completing the designs, since in many cases we are able to recommend a standard magnet already being produced, and in this manner effect a saving both in the cost of the magnets and the tools for producing them.

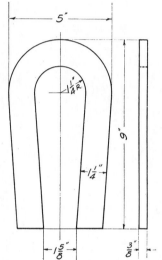

Fig. 27.—*Standard Mill Magnet Carried in Stock.*

In Fig. "27" are shown the dimensions of mill magnets commonly used; these are regularly carried in stock ready for shipment in any reasonable quantity.

Another magnet regularly manufactured by this company is that used for protecting vending machines from the use of iron slugs. Many different types of magnets have been used for this purpose, but the disadvantage of most of them has been the fact that they are unreliable in operation, and in some cases the throat of the machine becomes stopped up when a slug is inserted. In Fig. "29" is an illustration of a patented form of vending machine magnet designed by the author. This magnet is of such shape and is placed in such position that the instant the slug is inserted the tips of the poles attract it, the slug then rolls along the lower surface of the magnet until it reaches the point of minimum strength, when it drops into the box provided for receiving the slugs. This form of magnet has been found very

Page Twenty-nine

successful, it being found impossible to drive a slug by it, and it is also free from clogging.

SHIPPING.

Magnets are shipped in a magnetized or demagnetized condition, depending upon the desires of the customer. Every magnet manufactured by our company is tested for both magnetic strength and retentivity and has therefore been magnetized by us, so that the omission of this operation does not alter the price. The condition in which magnets are shipped does, however, affect the freight rates, since by the ruling of the Interstate Commerce Commission magnets not mag-

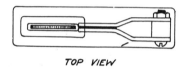

TOP VIEW

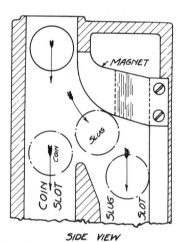

SIDE VIEW

Fig. 29.—Special Magnet for the Protection of Vending Machines Against the Use of Iron Slugs.

netized are classed as forgings, taking third-class rate, whereas charged magnets are given a first-class rate.

Whether shipped charged or demagnetized, we recommend that magnets be recharged by the purchaser at the proper stage in the process of assembly. It is important that the original polarity be maintained in the recharging process and, of course, any process looking to the stabilizing of the magnetic state must be carried out after the magnetic circuit has been completely assembled. Since these are matters peculiar to each particular design, it is impossible to fully cover them here.

MAGNET DESIGN AND TESTING.

Our company maintains an engineering department, fully equipped with the necessary apparatus for testing magnet steel, permanent magnets, instruments and magnetos. This enables us to cooperate with our customers in the design of permanent magnets for various purposes, the study of the performance of their equipment with magnets of different design, as well as the determination of the proper magnet to give the best result in each case.

A TRADE-MARKED PRODUCT.

From the beginning it has been our purpose to make a high-grade, uniform product, well adapted to the particular needs of each customer, and as a result of this policy have been able to develop what is perhaps by far the largest and most complete plant in this country, devoted exclusively to the manufacture of permanent magnets and electrical instruments.

Every magnet made by our company bears our trade mark, NE, which is a guarantee that it has been carefully and honestly made and tested, and further, that whether in the hands of the original or the ultimate purchaser, it still carries with it our unlimited guarantee of quality and that any inferior magnet of our manufacture sent to us will be replaced by a good one without cost.

reprinted from
Frick's Physical Techniques
A Manual for Experiments in Physics
by Dr J. Frick – 1878

CHAPTER V.

EXPERIMENTS ON MAGNETISM.

[213] Treatment of iron and steel for magnetic experiments.—Take good charcoal iron, forge it into the proper shape, and, after coating it with clay, heat it to redness. It becomes still softer if left to cool among the coals. Artificial magnets are made of the best English or German cast-steel, which may be had in almost any desired shape. It must not be raised above a dull-red heat, nor kept long even at this temperature. After forging it into the desired shape, finish it with a file. Great care is necessary in forging cast-steel; it must never be heated above a dark cherry red, nor must it be hammered cold.

In tempering the bar it must be held upright, and, if it be in the shape of a horseshoe, both poles must be plunged in together. This is the only way to prevent it from warping. The scale of oxide usually falls off in tempering, but the steel may be hard although this does not occur. It should be so hard as not to be attacked by the best files.

In this condition the steel is so brittle as to break to pieces *Fig.* 409. if it should fall on the floor. In order to prevent this, it must be polished and slowly tempered to a straw-yellow, over a bright charcoal fire. The fire may be fanned, but not blown with a bellows, which makes an irregular heat. When the steel attains its straw-yellow color, it must be quenched in cold water.

If the steel has warped in cooling, so as to be useless, it must be tempered blue. It loses thereby a part of its coercive force, but can be used for many purposes, and may be hammered into shape with a sharp-edged hammer, like fig. 409. The bar must be laid on the anvil and the blows struck close together on the concave side. With a little care, this may be done even when it is tempered yellow.

The north pole should be marked by a stroke with a file, or a letter **N** stamped upon it, before the steel is tempered. It may, however, be etched in with acid afterwards.

[214] Form of the magnets. — Bar magnets should be only about one-third or one-fourth as thick as they are broad, and not over a foot long. Horseshoe magnets are made somewhat longer, each limb being often a foot in length, and $1\frac{1}{2}$ to 2 inches in breadth. The poles of these magnets, whether they have the shape of a horseshoe, as in fig. 410, or straighter, as in fig. 411, should not be more than the breadth of the

Fig. 410.

Fig. 411.

Fig. 412.

bar from each other.   Bars which are much curved are difficult to magnetize, and very apt to warp in tempering.   It is best to have large steel bars tempered by a file-cutter.

[215] **Magnetic magazines.**—Powerful magnets are made by combining several bars in one.   The middle bar is sometimes made longer than the rest, fig. 412, but it is better to have them all of the same length.   Each bar is magnetized separately, and the whole bound together by brass bands or screws.   It is of no advantage to separate them by strips of brass, as is sometimes done.   If the bars are warped and cannot well be straightened without softening them, it is well to separate them, under the bands or screws, by a thin plate, in order to compensate for the irregularity.

Straight bars may be combined either by simple brass bands, or by caps

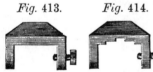

Fig. 413.   *Fig.* 414.

of soft iron screwed over their ends.   A simple plan is to bind them up tightly with brass wire, and drive little wedges of brass between them at proper places. Fig. 413 represents a cap for bars of equal, and fig. 414 one for bars of unequal length.   The binding screws are made of brass, because screws of strongly magnetized iron are unpleasant to drive.   These caps are called the armature of the magnet.   They may be attached also to horseshoe magnets, but they must be very carefully fitted on.

[216] **Preservation of magnets.**—The poles of both horseshoe and bar magnets must be connected by soft iron, in order to preserve their power.   Straight bars are armed by laying them parallel, at a little

distance apart, with the opposite poles next each other, and joining the two ends, as in fig. 415. For horseshoe magnets, this piece of iron is called the anchor, and is usually furnished with a hook, to which weights may be attached. Fig. 412 represents a horseshoe magnet with its anchor. The anchor is sometimes made with a slightly convex face, but an even surface seems to be better. The anchor must be comparatively thick, so that when attached, its lower side will have very little attractive power. It is not necessary to keep the anchor of the magnet always loaded with weights in order to preserve it in good condition. Rust does not diminish the power of a magnet, except by preventing the close contact of the anchor. To keep them from rusting, they may be rubbed with a greasy rag after being used. Magnets should be guarded from blows or concussions, and not rubbed with any hard substance, especially with iron, nor laid upon iron. Heat is still more injurious to the power of a magnet; even a temperature of 40° C. has a perceptible effect.

Fig. 415.

[217] **Armature of natural magnets.**—The position of the poles is ascertained by rolling the loadstone in iron filings, and two parallel faces cut perpendicular to the axis. The other sides of the magnet are also cut, so as to give it somewhat the shape of a parallelopipedon. Over the poles are laid two iron plates, figs. 416 and 417, the size of the face, bent over at the top, and terminating below in projections p. The under surfaces of these projections must lie in the same

Fig. 418.   *Fig. 419.*

Fig. 416.   *Fig. 417.*

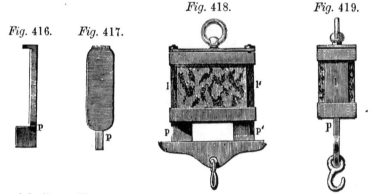

straight line. The magnet is supported by shoulders on these projections. These two plates are connected by brass bands, and an anchor laid on the two ends. The magnet may be hung up by a ring attached to a crosspiece of iron, as shown in figs. 418 and 419.

The power of natural magnets may be increased by laying them between the poles of a powerful electro-magnet.

[218] **Magnetic needles.**—There should be several of these, of various lengths and different degrees of sensitiveness. The only difficulty in making them is in suspending them on pivots. It is very easy to suspend the needle by a cocoon-fibre, and cover it with a glass case, but this arrangement does not answer for most purposes. Delicate needles should be supported on pivots turning in caps of agate; and as the manufacture of these is difficult, it is better to buy the needles ready made, or at least the agate caps, which are not very expensive.

To set an agate cap in a needle, fix a piece of stout brass wire to a chuck on the lathe, bore in it a hole, a little smaller than the hole in the needle, and deeper than the thickness of the cap and needle together. Enlarge this hole to the depth of a millimeter, just sufficiently to admit of the cap being forced into it, and turn the brass off thin to the same depth on the outside. Set in the cap, and press the brass tightly down upon it with a burnisher. Fig. 420 represents an enlarged section of the wire and cap. Next, turn off the wire to just the size of the hole in the needle. If the needle is of the shape represented in fig. 427, the apex of the conical cavity need not be much above the needle; but if it be thin, like fig. 425, the cavity must project 1 or 2 millimeters. In the latter case it is well to make a little shoulder on the brass ring, as shown in fig. 421.

Fig. 420.

Fig. 421.   *Fig.* 422.   *Fig.* 423.

After cutting off the wire, fix the cap in a block and widen the hole a little below, as seen in fig. 422. If the cap be too large to pass through the hole in the needle with its brass collar, the wire must be turned off, as represented in fig. 423, inserted from above, and fastened by driving a conical steel punch into the hole below. Glass caps answer tolerably well. A suitable piece of glass may be cut out of a thick plate, by means of a copper ring (§ 15,) and the conical cavity drilled with a three-cornered file and spirits of turpentine. It must afterwards be ground smooth with fine emery on wood, and polished with rouge. The cavity may be bored after the glass is set in brass.

Where great delicacy is not required, which is most frequently the case, a very simple contrivance answers the purpose. Bend a strip of brass, about a line in width, fig. 424, over the hole in the needle, and make a little depression in it with a steel punch. This is both simpler and better than to drill out a cap of brass or steel. A similar *Fig. 424.* depression made in the needle itself, while lying on a plate of lead, will insure sufficient stability and mobility.

The needles may be made of various shapes, as represented in figs. 425, 426, and 427. The first two are made of watch-spring, the last of bar

Fig. 425.

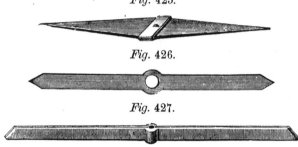

Fig. 426.

Fig. 427.

steel. The hole in the center is made to receive the cap. They must be cleaned and polished before tempering. In tempering, the needles should be laid on a sheet of iron, or fastened to a wire, instead of being held in the tongs, which prevents their being uniformly heated. The south end of the needle may either be made heavier than the north end, or loaded with a strip of brass, like fig. 424, made to slide upon it.

Fine sewing needles answer very well in most cases. They may be fastened into a base of wood or brass. For very delicate magnetic needles, the support must be made of steel. File a piece of steel sharp, and screw or rivet the blunt end into a brass foot; fasten this on a lathe, and sharpen the point with a fine file moistened with oil, turning meanwhile very rapidly, and moving the file back and forth. The point of the needle is next hardened and afterwards polished with a fine whet- *Fig. 428.* stone on the lathe. The point must appear sharp when examined with a lens. The support need not, generally, be very high. Fig. 428 represents one of natural size.

[219] **The compass.**—For many experiments in magnetism and electricity, a compass, that is, a delicate magnetic needle moving over a graduated circle, and protected by a glass case, is indispensable. For Weber's experiments, the needle must not be over 1 or 2 inches in length. With so small a diameter the divisions of the arc cannot be made less than 2 degrees, and even with the greatest care, the errors must be very great. It is better, therefore, in this case, to fasten a

thin thread of black glass to each end of the needle, parallel to the axis.
The form represented in fig. 427 is well adapted to this purpose by filing
a groove in the back, as represented in enlarged section in fig. 429.   The
circle may now be made 4 inches in diameter, and a greater
Fig 429. degree of accuracy be attained, even by hand-division, than is
possible with a smaller circle on the graduating machine.   If
the circle be made on paper, it should first be pasted on a board,
about ½ an inch thick, and then graduated.   The pivot upon
which the needle turns must not project much above the board, and even
then a large error of parallax may occur in reading off.   This is best
avoided by excavating the inner surface of the circle, and inserting in it a
mirror: the point where the glass thread and its image coincide, will give
the true reading.   A narrow ring of pasteboard, pasted around a circular
plate of glass, may serve as a case for the instrument.   The needle should
be taken off its support when not in use.   If the board is in the shape
of a parallelogram, and the median line of the graduation parallel to one
of the sides, the compass will serve for the approximate determination of
the declination or of the geographical meridian.

To preserve the pivot of a compass from injury, the needle must be
raised from it whenever it is not in use.   An arrangement is usually made
to effect this without lifting the glass cover.   In fig. 430 *b a c* represents

Fig. 430.

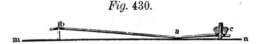

a bent brass lever, terminating at both ends in a perforated disk.   It rests
at *a* in a little cavity in the base of the compass.   By pressing the screw
c, the end *b* raises the needle against the glass case cover of the compass;
when the screw is loosened, the lever sinks by its own weight.

To test the delicacy of a magnetic needle, set it in vibration by bringing
near it a piece of iron.   Its position on the graduated circle may be
accurately noted, and a piece of iron brought near, so as to draw it a little
to one side; when the iron is slowly withdrawn, the needle must return
exactly to its former position.

Instead of supporting the needle on a pivot, it may, for many purposes,
be suspended by a cocoon fiber, as represented in fig. 431.   The needle is
thus made very sensitive, but cannot be used to show the effect of a second
magnet upon it, because the attraction of the magnet draws it out of the
center of the graduation.*

---

* It may be remarked, by the way, that the magnetic needle must not be observed
through steel spectacles.

[220] **Magnetizing.**—At the present day large steel magnets are seldom or never used; in place of them we have electro-magnets, which can be made of any degree of power required. These electro-magnets enable us to magnetize to saturation the largest bars of steel, by a very simple process. The many methods which have been devised for making strong magnets from weak ones are therefore of little importance to us, the so-called single and double touch and Hoffer's method answering every purpose.

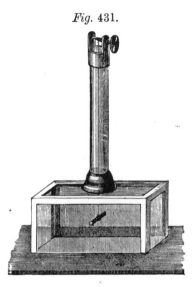

Fig. 431.

[221] **The single touch.**— The simplest method of performing this, is to stroke the end intended for the north pole on each side about 10 times with the south pole of a magnet, beginning in the middle and bringing the magnet back in a curve through the air. The same process is repeated with the north pole, on the other end. From 10 to 20 strokes will give all the power which the magnet is capable of imparting. The new magnet may be fastened to the table, by a piece of iron in the center, which will have a tendency to determine the neutral point to this position. The magnetism is stronger and more uniformly distributed, by setting the opposite ends of two equally strong magnets upon the center of the bar, so as to make an angle of 80° with each other, and drawing them slowly asunder, preserving the same inclination. In this case also the magnets must be returned to the starting-point through the air. The end which is touched with the north pole becomes the south pole. This method is better than any other for making magnetic needles or bars to be used in measurements. A horseshoe bar is treated in the same way, only the anchor is placed on it when it is touched with two magnets at once, or with both limbs of another horseshoe magnet. The anchor is held fast, and the pole of the touching magnet carried over it. When a straight bar is touched with a horseshoe magnet, the surface of the latter must be held perpendicular to the bar.

Fig. 432

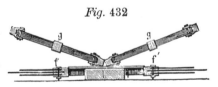

A bar treated in this way becomes still stronger by placing it between the opposite poles (ff', fig. 432,) of two powerful magnets. The bar must be supported by a wooden block l.

[222] **The double touch.**—This method consists in laying the two poles of a horseshoe magnet, or two equally strong bars, together upon the middle of the bar to be magnetized, and moving them slowly back and forward 10 or 20 times over its whole length; this is repeated on both sides of the bar. The motion must cease in the middle of the bar, so that each end shall receive an equal number of strokes. If a horseshoe magnet be used for this purpose, its two poles must be very close together, otherwise it almost inevitably produces succession points. If two bar magnets

Fig. 433.

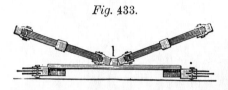

be used, their poles may be brought very near together, but should be kept from actual contact by a bit of wood (l, fig 433,) placed between them. The magnets are held at an angle of 15 to 20° with a bar.

In this case, as in the other, the effect is considerably increased by laying the ends of the bar on two strong magnets. The touching poles must be the same as those of the supporting magnets next them respectively; the poles of the new magnet will be the opposite of those upon which they rest. In magnetizing a horseshoe bar, it is an advantage to attach the anchor, the magnet being stronger even after this is removed.

[223] **Hoffer's method** of the double touch consists in placing an anchor before the horseshoe bar to be magnetized, and passing over it the two poles of a horseshoe magnet, either from the end toward the curve or in the contrary direction, as represented in figs. 434 and 435. In the

<table>
<tr><td style="text-align:center">*Fig. 434.*</td><td style="text-align:center">*Fig. 435.*</td></tr>
<tr><td>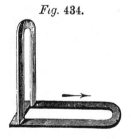</td><td>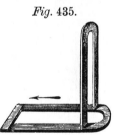</td></tr>
</table>

first case, the poles of the new magnet will be the same as the inducing magnet; in the latter, they will be the contrary. The inducing magnet must, of course, be of the same width as the other. By this method a maximum effect can be produced in ten strokes, and it is one of the best known. Bars can be magnetized in the same way by laying them parallel, with an armature at each end. If the inducing magnet be heavy, to avoid the labor of moving it, it may be clamped to a table with its ends projecting, as seen in fig. 436, and the bar carried over it. With electro-magnets the conductors render this arrangement necessary.

Fig. 436.

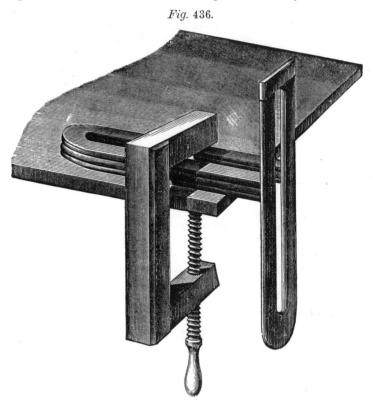

[224] Large magnets have always less power, in proportion to their weight. According to Häcker, if M be the weight supported, and p the weight of the magnet, $M = a \sqrt[3]{p^2}$, in which a is a constant factor, varying with the quality and temper of the steel. Häcker found this factor in some cases equal to $39\frac{8}{10}$, which may be considered very satisfactory, though it has been exceeded in a few instances. This gives us an easy method of testing and comparing the strength of magnets. The experiment may be made, by laying successively small weights (coarse shot for instance) in a pan attached to the armature of the magnet. The point of attachment must be so adjusted that the armature will part at the same time on both

sides.   Of course, the contact surface of the armature must be horizontal. This method, however, does not give exact results.   The only good method of testing the quality of magnetic needles and bars is by oscillation. The bars may be suspended for the purpose in a brass stirrup, by a thread of unwrought silk.   According to Häcker, if T be the time of one oscillation in seconds, p the weight, and a the length of the magnet, $T = c \sqrt[3]{p} \sqrt[5]{a}$, in which c equals $2 \frac{3.5}{100}$, p being expressed in Bavarian loths, and a in Paris inches.   To show the attraction and repulsion of

Fig. 437.

magnets, suspend the bar magnet, about 6 or 8 inches in length, in a stirrup of paper or brass, by several threads of unwrought silk, as shown in fig 437.   To make the same experiment with a natural magnet, fasten a ribbon around its middle and suspend it in the same way.

[225] **Distribution of magnetism.** — For these experiments we need clean, fine iron filings, and a number of small bars of soft iron, from $\frac{1}{2}$ to 2 inches in length and of various thicknesses.   These may be made of good iron wire, their ends filed round and well annealed.

(*a*) *Magnetic curves.*   Sift fine iron filings upon a plate of glass or a sheet of stiff paper, under which a magnetic bar is held; a few gentle taps of the finger will cause the iron filings to arrange themselves in curves. The same process serves to show the succession points in a magnetic bar.

Magnetic bars with succession points are produced with most certainty by means of a powerful horseshoe magnet and the double touch.

(*b*) A magnet brought near two needles, suspended near each other by silk threads, causes a mutual repulsion.

(*c*) Dip the similar poles of two magnets in iron filings and bring them close together, the projecting filaments of iron filings will repel each other; but if the opposite poles be taken, the filaments will interlock, like the arms of a polyp around its prey.

[226] Iron exposed to the inductive influence of a magnet while red hot, and suddenly cooled, remains magnetic.   This is most easily shown with iron filings and a horseshoe magnet.   A thick bunch of the iron filings may be taken up between the poles of the magnet; reduce this to about the breadth of a finger and half that thickness.   Heat this with a spirit-lamp and a blow-pipe, and cool it suddenly.   The middle portion will cohere, and will be found to have the properties of a magnet.   A powerful electro-magnet answers best for this purpose.

[227] **Declination of the needle.**—In order to give a distinct idea of the direction of a magnetic needle, it is well to designate the meridian in the lecture room by means of plummets. For this purpose, fasten to the ceiling three firm iron hooks, upon which the plummets may be suspended, with a sharp incision in each, to designate the position of the thread. Balls of lead may be used for the plummets. Place a long sensitive needle on a rectangular board, and divide the circle by hand, so that the diameter from which the graduation begins shall be parallel to the side of the rectangle. This diameter can be easily fixed in the line of the astronomical meridian, and the declination determined approximately in degrees. The simplest mode of determining the meridian depends upon the situation of the room, and therefore no general directions can be given for it.

[228] **Dip of the needle.**—The following experiment is instructive as preparatory to the explanation of the dip of the needle : Lay a bar magnet, about a foot long, on the table, and balance a bit of magnetized knitting-needle on a fine thread. If the needle be carried back and forth over the bar, it will stand horizontal over the middle, while toward either end the opposite pole will dip downward. The best mode of suspending the needle is by passing it through a cork, and balancing it on an axis supported on wire hooks, as shown in fig. 438. Neither the declination nor the dip need be de-

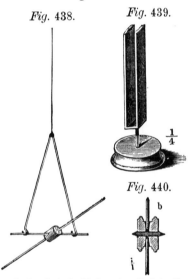

Fig. 438.   *Fig.* 439.

Fig. 440.

termined accurately for purposes of illustration ; for measuring the latter approximately, we may use a magnetic needle, 5 or 6 inches in length, with an axis pointed, and furnished with screw threads on both sides, fig. 440. The axis passes loosely through the hole in the needle, and is fastened by two nuts, *a* and *b*. The axis must be adjusted accurately in the center of gravity of the needle, after screwing the nuts moderately tight. The needle is fixed on a support like fig. 439, which consists of a brass fork fastened in a wooden base. Fig. 441 shows the upper end of natural size. The inner superior edge of each side of the fork is filed out cylindrically, and polished with emery, so that only the points of the steel axis will rest upon these surfaces. The plane of rotation of the needle must be made to coincide with the magnetic meridian. As it can be no longer shown,

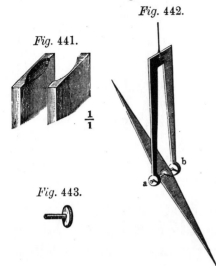

Fig. 442.

Fig. 441.

$\frac{1}{1}$

Fig. 443.

after the needle is once magnetized, that it was previously in equilibrium, the poles must be reversed, to show that the north pole will always dip toward the earth.

The needle may also be suspended in the manner seen in fig. 442. The axis is supported by two steel screws, like fig. 443, each of which has a little conical cavity in the end. This apparatus assumes of itself the direction of the magnetic meridian, but must be very carefully constructed.

The simplest apparatus is the one in fig. 438, already described. Thrust a bit of unmagnetic knitting-needle through the cork so that it will rest in a horizontal position, then cut away the cork below, or stick wax on it above, so as to throw the center of gravity in the axis. The needle may then be magnetized and its poles reversed at pleasure.

[229] **Influence of terrestrial magnetism on iron.**—This may be shown by means of a delicate magnetic needle, and a bar of soft iron, 3 or 4 feet in length, which must be well heated, and used for no other purpose, because any mechanical action upon iron gives it some retentive power for magnetism. Hold the bar in the direction of the dipping needle, and bring a small sensitive needle alternately near the upper and the lower end. The poles are reversed by inverting the bar. Hammering it while under the inductive influence of the earth will impart to it a degree of permanent magnetism

reprinted from
First Steps in Magnetism
by W. Jerome Harrison
revised by W. L. Weber – 1901

VIII.—METHODS OF MAGNETIZATION.

42. How to make Permanent Magnets—43. Method of Single Touch—44. Method of Separate Touch—45. Method of Double Touch—46. Consequent Points—47. Degree of Magnetization—48. How to make an Electro-magnet.

42. How to make Permanent Magnets.—If we accept the theory of "polarity of the molecules," we can understand that in what we should call an "unmagnetized" bar of steel every molecule is really a magnet, but that, as there is no *arrangement* of the molecules—as their poles lie pointing in all directions—so the bar, as a whole, has none of the properties of a magnet. But if we can introduce an orderly arrangement among the molecules—if we can force them, or most of them, to lie so that all their N.-seeking poles point in one direction, and all their S.-seeking poles in the other, then the bar will exhibit magnetic properties.

According to the two-fluid theory, the act of magnetization will consist in the *separation* of the two magnetic fluids which exist in a state of combination around each molecule. When these fluids are separated, so that the north magnetic fluid is brought entirely to the same end of each molecule—leaving south magnetic fluid at the other end—then the whole bar becomes a magnet,

110

43. Method of Single Touch.—Take a piece of steel, a sewing-needle for instance, and stroke it several times, always in the *same direction* and with the *same pole* of a bar magnet (Fig. 25), stroke it also

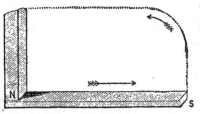

on each side. Of course, whether we stroke the needle with the magnet, or rub the magnet with the needle, will make no difference; the needle

Fig. 25.—Method of Single Touch. will quickly become a magnet. If we test the new magnet, we shall find that the end where the magnet was *taken away* from the steel is a pole of the *opposite name* to that with which it was rubbed. Thus, if we rub the needle from eye to point with a N.-seeking pole, then the point will become a S.-seeking pole; if we rub it the same way with a S.-seeking pole, then the point will be made a N.-seeking pole. We can imagine the north magnetism dragging the south magnetism after it, attracting the S.-seeking poles of all the molecules, and forcing them all to point in one direction. This method is usually employed only to magnetize *small* pieces of steel.

44. Method of Separate Touch.—Two magnets are required for this method, and their *opposite* poles must be employed. Commence in the centre of the bar to be magnetized, and *separate* the two magnets, moving one towards one end of the bar, and the other in the opposite direction. Lift up both the magnets when they reach the ends of the bar, and commence with them again in the middle (see Fig.

26)   Repeat the process on each side of the bar, giving each side, say, half-a-dozen rubs.   In this, as

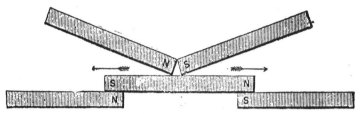

FIG. 26.—Separate Touch.

in the next method, it will be found advantageous to support the ends of the bar to be magnetized upon two magnets, arranged with their poles as in Fig. 26. The presence of these magnets enables the steel bar to be magnetized more rapidly and more effectually, for the attractive forces of their poles prevent the molecules of the bar from slipping round (on the molecular polarity theory), or the recombination of the two fluids (on the two-fluid theory), in the intervals during which the magnets are being raised and moved from the ends to the centre of the bar.

45. Method of Double Touch.—As in the last

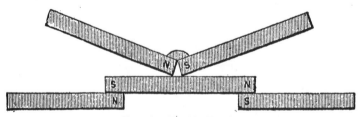

FIG. 27.—Double Touch.

method, use the opposite poles of two bar magnets, but place a piece of cork or of wood between them, to prevent the ends touching (Fig. 27).   Commence in the *middle* of the steel bar to be magnetized, and

move the two magnets *together,* first to one end of
the bar, and then right back to the other end.   Leave
off in the middle, taking care to give each half of
the bar the same number of rubs.   Repeat this
process on the opposite side of the steel bar, and, if
the bar be of any thickness, on the other two sides
also.

*Permanent magnetization of steel by the electric
current.*—The most rapid and easy method of mag-

netizing ordinary steel
bars is to pass them
through a coil of silk-
covered copper wire,
through which a strong
current of electricity
is flowing (Fig. 28).
Care must be taken

FIG. 28.—Steel bar passed through coil of
wire carrying current.

always to pass the bar through the coil with *the
same end first.*   We must consider that the electric
current causes the molecules of steel to place themselves so that their like poles all point in the same
direction.

46. Consequent Points.—When the steel bar or rod
is very long as compared with its thickness, as in the
case of a knitting-needle, for example, or when it
is incorrectly magnetized—either accidentally or on
purpose—we may have four, six, eight, or more
poles in the same bar of steel.   In this case we may
consider the bar as composed of two, three, or four
magnets placed end to end, and *not* that we have
one magnet with four or more poles.   The additional
poles situated at various parts of the bar are called

113

"consequent points," or "consequent poles" (Fig. 29). They may be readily discovered by the curves which will proceed from them if we lay a piece of cardboard or glass upon the bar, and strew some iron filings upon it.

Fig 29.—Consequent points or poles in steel magnet.

In this way it is possible to obtain a bar of steel which shall have a N.-seeking pole *at each end;* but we must not think that we have obtained a magnet with a single pole. Careful experiments will prove that in such a case there are two S.-seeking poles situated close together somewhere in the middle of the bar (Fig. 30).

Fig. 30.—Consequent points, with N pole at each end.

47. **Degree of Magnetization.**—When a bar of steel has developed the full amount of magnetism which it is capable of *permanently retaining,* it is said to be *saturated.* The bar may be magnetized beyond this point, but the extra power so acquired is soon lost; in such a case we might say that the bar was *super-saturated.*

48. **How to make an Electro-magnet.**—Temporary, or electro-magnets, consist of pieces of soft iron, round which copper wire has been coiled (see Fig. 9). The wire must be covered with cotton, or, better, with silk, and it must be wound round the iron always in the same direction. The greater portion of the wire may be laid, coil upon coil, round the two *ends* of the soft iron bar, since no matter how strong a current of electricity we pass round

the *middle* of the iron bar, we know that it can
there produce no outward effect, for that is the
position of the neutral line.   It has been found, by
actual experiment, that when a very powerful electric current is passed round an iron bar (thus rendering it a magnet) the bar becomes a little *longer*.
This is probably caused by the molecules turning
round so as to set themselves parallel to the axis of
the bar (see Fig. 32).

More Ideas

An exact explanation of why certain materials are magnetic while others are not is deeply rooted in solid-state physics - the physics of matter. If you intend to create permanent magnets or merely experiment with them, acquiring basic theoretical knowledge is well worth the trouble.

Since such theory is beyond the scope of this simple book, you'll want to acquire scientific texts for your reference library. In the next few pages, we'll quickly expose you to terms and concepts that'll you'll want to investigate. Our explanation is superficial at best. So take the strange terms mentioned below and research them in college physics texts and in the texts mentioned in the bibliography.

Top rate books can be found in engineering libraries at major universities and can be purchased from used book dealers. Just a few books can dramatically expand your knowledge of magnetism and will help you be more successful in your experiments and inventions.

Source of Magnetism

Atoms are made up of protons and neutrons in the nucleus which is surrounded by electrons traveling in unique orbits. An electron spins like a top in one of two possible directions. Moving electrons and spinning electrons generate magnetic fields. If two electrons with opposite spins pair off, their magnetic fields cancel. An unpaired electron will add to the atom's overall magnetic moment. An important concept to investigate here is the Pauli exclusion principle because it directly contributes to the Hund rules which predict which elements in the periodic table should be magnetic based on their electronic structure.

Members of the transition metals portion of the periodic table have unusual electron clouds that produce electrical conductivity and may or may not produce a noticeable magnetic moment. In the fourth row, important elements include manganese (Mn), iron (Fe), cobalt (Co), and nickel (Ni), which all have large magnetic moments. These are known as ferromagnetic materials.

Diamagnetic Materials

Many materials have completely paired spinning electrons which prevents each individual atom of that material from exhibiting any net magnetic moment. These are what we call non-magnetic materials.

Paramagnetic Materials

Here, each atom has some magnetic moment, but heat, which makes electrons vibrate wildly, prevents the electrons from all pointing in the same direction. The magnetic field of one atom cancels out the magnetic field of its neighbor. Under normal circumstances, the material is not magnetic.

If the paramagnetic material is subjected to an outside magnetic field, or magnetizing force (usually referred to as an H field), the field will be stronger than the random vibrations, and at least some atoms will begin to line up in the same direction so that their individual magnetic fields aid instead of cancel one another. The result is that the material is now magnetic. The degree to which the atoms are willing to magnetically line up will determine how strongly magnetic the material becomes.

As might be expected, cooling the material lowers the random vibrations of the electrons enabling them to line up more easily, thus producing a stronger magnetic moment. This is predicted by the Curie law.

Ferromagnetic Materials

Each atom of a ferromagnetic material exhibits a strong magnetic moment, and large numbers of atoms come together to create a "domain." These domains possess strong magnetic moment, yet the overall material may not be magnetic because the domains do not line up. The domain magnetic fields fight one another and cancel each other out.

The techniques described in this book work because they line up all of the domain magnetic moments in the same direction, allowing them to help one another. Once this is accomplished, the material is said to be a permanent magnet, or is said to be magnetized. If every domain in the material is properly lined up, no more additional magnetic moment can be created, and the material is said to be saturated.

Suitable Materials

In Gilbert's day, the early 1600's, hard steel was the best material available for magnet manufacture. As late as the 1880's magnets were still being made with 1% steel, quench hardened and usually tempered. Wrought iron, or annealed low-carbon steel (soft iron) which would not create a permanent magnetic field (low retentivity) was used as pole pieces. Because the science of metallurgy did not exist, the physical properties of early steel were unpredictable.

In the 1890's metallurgists found that adding small amounts of tungsten and chromium to steel would significantly improve the alloy's magnetic properties.

Later, large amounts of cobalt were added. About 1920 Honda discovered that complex alloys of steel that included cobalt, manganese, chromium and tungsten could give even better performance.

Then came Mishima's alnico alloys composed of aluminum, nickel and cobalt which were usually melted and cast. The metal was cooled in the presence of a strong magnetic field, producing really high quality magnets.

Ceramic magnetic materials were developed by molding and baking oxides of iron, barium and strontium. These oxides, often held together with a rubber-like compound, are used, for instance, as magnetic gaskets in modern refrigerators.

The newest magnetic materials exploit rare-earth compounds such as neodymium, samarium, dysprosium, and gadolinium. If you have deep pockets you may want to experiment with an alloy of 77% platinum and 23% cobalt.

H Fields

Excite a material with a magnetizing force, and it may or may not respond. A magnetizing force may come from within the material itself, from the earth's natural magnetic field, the field of a permanent magnet, or an extremely intense field from a pulsed electromagnet. These are magnetizing forces, commonly referred to as H fields. In the cgs system of units, H is measured in Oersteds, while in the mks system, the unit is ampere-turns or amperes per meter. H is also known as magnetomotive force per unit length.

A magnetic material responds to H by creating a magnetic field. Lines of such a field are called flux. The intensity of a magnetic field can be specified as flux per unit area, much like the air pressure in a tire is specified as pounds per square inch. This is the B field. Cgs units are gauss, still commonly used. In mks units, flux is measure in webers, so B field is webers per square meter, also called a Tesla. Ten thousand gauss equal one Tesla.

Although this is really confusing at first, the important thing to remember is that exposing a material to an H field results in a B field. One material exposed to a number of Oersteds of H field, might respond by generating a certain number of gauss, while another might generate twice as many gauss, (or webers per square meter). The latter material is obviously superior. The ratio of B generated by a given amount of H is called permeability. High permeability in a magnetic material is usually desirable.

Permeability is not constant in most ferromagnetic materials, but changes in a complex manner as excitation changes. If a graph of H versus B is plotted, we get a hysteresis curve. The fact that the graph is made up of curves and not straight lines is an indication of changing permeability.

The second quadrant (upper left) of a hysterisis is of special interest. On the vertical axis is the maximum B field generated, while on the horizontal axis is the negative H field, or more commonly referred to as the demagnetizing force. You want a permanent magnet to have as much B field as possible yet not demagnetize until the reverse H field is very high. An excellent measure of permanent magnet quality is the product of B and H, called the BHmax, or energy of the magnet. The energy may be specified in cgs units of m.g.o., or millions of gauss-oersteds. In mks units, it's called thousand-tesla-amperes per meter.

An early, common alnico alloy might produce a magnet with 11 thousand-tesla-amperes per meter of energy. A later alnico alloy might
118

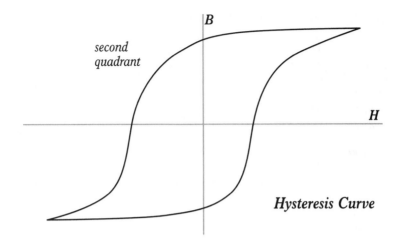

second quadrant

B

H

Hysteresis Curve

produce a magnet with 42. Platinum-cobalt might give 75, while common ceramics might only have 25. A rare-earth magnet like samarium-cobalt will usually exhibit more than a 100 thousand-tesla-amperes per meter of energy.

Possibilities

It is possible to build very powerful magnets from nothing more than hardened carbon steel. Creating magnets by stroking, such as in the double touch, cannot magnetize a thick bar of steel completely, that is, the domains in the center of the bar cannot be saturated. A far better approach is to magnetize thin pieces of steel completely and combine them into a compound magnet as described on page 99 of this book.

On page 45 it is noted that artificial magnets can not lift more than 30 times their own weight. Physicist, J. C. Jamin, claimed to have built, in the mid 1870's, a compound magnet from from thin steel strips which were bent around one another to form a large horseshoe magnet. One of his magnets weighing about a 100 pounds could lift over a thousand pounds. So, although this is only a factor of ten, it is nonetheless possible to build very powerful magnets with the primitive techniques discussed in this book.

In the 1770's Gowin Knight created a "magnetic magazine" by assembling 240 bars, 1" wide, by 1/2" thick, by 15" long into a compound magnet of exceptional power. Later the bars were rearranged into a large horseshoe magnet that was used by Michael Faraday to build his classic copper disk electrical generator that today so intrigues the perpetual motion crowd.

Terms

When dealing with magnetism, names, definitions and units are anything but uniform. Different scientists and engineers use the same term in different ways. To be a top rate magnet experimenter you need to understand the principles behind such terms as:

coercivity, Curie temperature, demagnetizing force, eddy currents, energy product maximum: BHmax, Gauss, Gilbert, hysteresis curve or loop, induction, residual induction, flux, flux density, Oersted, Weber, magnetizing force, magnetomotive force, Maxwell (not Jack Benny's automobile), permeability, reluctance, retentivity, remanence, Hall effect

Bibliography

The single most important tool you need for experimenting with permanent magnets is knowledge. And that means you must begin building a reference library if you haven't already. Below are a number of quality books worth having. Most are no longer printed, but can still be found through antiquarian book dealers.

You should have these two books...

L. R. Moskowitz. PERMANENT MAGNET DESIGN AND APPLICATION HANDBOOK. Boston: Cahners Books Intl 1976 – other editions reprinted by Krieger
Everything you could want to know about creating permanent magnets including designs for powerful impulse magnetizers and demagnetizers. Practical how-to for industry. Very highly recommended.

R. J. Parker and R. J. Studders. PERMANENT MAGNETS AND THEIR APPLICATIONS. New York: Wiley, 1962
Excellent overview of magnet physics with practical how-to. Chapter one is reprint of classic magnet history reprinted from ENDEAVOR, Vol XVII, No 65, Jan 1958.

These are worth considering...

R. A. Dunlap. EXPERIMENTAL PHYSICS. New York: Oxford Univ Press 1988
The last chapter is a short but practical survey of magnetism and magnetic measurements.

A. H. Morrish. THE PHYSICAL PRINCIPLES OF MAGNETISM. New York: Wiley 1965

S. Chikazumi and S. H. Charap. PHYSICS OF MAGNETISM. Florida: Krieger Pub Co, 1986 reprint of 1964 original by Wiley
More information than you'll ever absorb. Written for scientists and engineers. Not for the average person, but top quality.